ι∪ι1 Promotion

in our Schools

Supplied by :-

T A L C
P.O.Box 49
St. Albans
Herts. AL1 5TX U.K

Tel: 44 (0) 1727 853869
Fax: 44 (0) 1727 846852

This book is available from
TALC
PO Box 49
St Albans
Herts AL1 4AX
United Kingdom

Health Promotion in our Schools

EDITED BY
Hugh Hawes

ILLUSTRATED BY
David Gifford

The Child-to-Child Trust
in association with UNICEF

Health Promotion in our Schools has been produced by the Child-to-Child Trust with financial assistance from MISEREOR, UNICEF and the British Council.

Cover Photographs:
Front: Clare Hanbury
Back: Anthea Sieveking

First published 1997

ISBN 0-946182-10-8

Designed by John C. Wright
Typeset by Domino Design Solutions
Printed by Werner Söderström Oy

Contents

Child-to-Child and UNICEF dedicate this book to Rajalakshmi Muralidharan in memory of her outstanding contribution to the education of children in India and to the Child-to-Child movement worldwide.

Preface

The idea of this book originated from the Child-to-Child Trust. Those working with Child-to-Child ideas and approaches in London and around the world have for long been committed to the concept of health action in schools.

The concepts of the *health-promoting school* and of *comprehensive school health education and promotion* as discussed and defined by the World Health Organization (WHO), as well as that of *life skills* developed by UNICEF have evolved parallel to ideas from Child-to-Child. This book unites them and at the same time links them with the minimum health content promoted in the book *Facts for Life*.

The making of this book has reflected this partnership. It has been developed by the Child-to-Child Trust in London with support from the education cluster in UNICEF and in consultation with the health education and health promotion unit in WHO. It has been read and criticized by all three bodies and also by two teams comprising health and education personnel from India and Ghana who have been closely involved in relevant field projects.

The following have been involved in developing and reviewing the material:

Paul Ackom *(Ghana)*
Indu Balagopal *(India)**
Rachel Carnegie *(UK)**
Fay Chung *(UNICEF, New York)**
Cyril Dalais *(UNICEF, New York)**
Fr. E. Mariampillai *(India)*
V. Gauthamdas *(India)*
David Gifford *(UK), illustrator**
Patricia Harman *(UK)*
Hugh Hawes *(UK) Editor**

Jack Jones *(WHO, Geneva)**
Jose Mathew *(India)*
K. Morris-Mensah *(Ghana)*
David Morley *(UK)*
Shobhna Reddy *(India)*
Christiana Obeng *(Ghana)*
Christine Scotchmer *(UK)**
David Stephens *(Ghana/UK)**
Andrew Tomkins *(UK)*
Veda Zachariah *(India)*

Those starred (*) attended or sent detailed comments to a review meeting in London in October 1996 which made final recommendations about content. In addition many others have been consulted at different times on points of detail. To all our deep-felt thanks.

In any book the final text must be chosen by one person who has to make decisions on what to retain and what to leave out. As editor I have to make these choices and take full responsibility for them.

Hugh Hawes

INTRODUCTION

Why this book has been written

This book is written for those who believe that good health in our schools is both necessary now and an investment for our future. It seeks to give ideas to all those who want to make schools healthier and to develop them as places which promote better health.

Health promotion involves all the health learning and health action which takes place in the school:

- the health services in a school;
- school policy and management practice in relation to health;
- the nutrition provided to school children;
- the hygiene and sanitation in the school;
- the teaching and learning that takes place in it;
- actions to spread health from school to the community.

All these must be linked together if we are to have what many people are calling *health-promoting schools*.

This is a book of ideas for those who plan, organize and promote health in schools and who wish these schools to become *health promoting*. It is not a manual for teachers. It focuses on all the six aspects we have listed but particularly on the teaching and learning about health which takes place in class and out of it. Throughout it emphasizes the prime importance of *children* as partners in health promotion.

Its target is schools that provide basic education – that is, the first nine or ten years of schooling in countries where resources are scarce and children are many. The typical schools which we write for will have many constraints. There will be large classes, overworked teachers, some with less education and training than they would wish, modest buildings and restricted materials. But these schools have many strengths which we can develop. They have well-motivated children who are eager to learn. They have heads and teachers who are well respected in communities. They have families who are interested and committed to their children's education, and communities (in rural areas particularly) which often have a sense of solidarity and cohesion and, above all, a real desire that children should be healthy, happy and successful at school.

This book is written to be read and used by different people at a number of levels. Each has different responsibilities, and together they can be most effective. That is why *in every chapter in the book* we have a special panel which shows how the ideas can be used at different levels.

THIS BOOK CAN HELP ...

POLICY MAKERS and INTERNATIONAL AGENCIES who advise national bodies managing health and education: this book can help them develop a comprehensive and integrated approach to health promotion in schools.

PROGRAMME DESIGNERS for health promotion and health education: they can find ideas about how national priorities and guidelines can be set, how programmes can be designed that encourage schools and teachers to become *active* in thinking about and promoting health. This book can also help them to think out how local areas and schools can be encouraged to set their own priorities and guidelines within the national framework.

LOCAL PLANNERS, MANAGERS and TRAINERS who plan and execute health promotion programmes together with NGOs, teachers' associations and similar bodies: this book can help them plan and organize locally based health projects and training programmes based on identified needs and priorities.

HEADS, TEACHERS and LOCAL HEALTH WORKERS and the **COMMUNITIES** they serve: this book can enable them to find out how to organize health for the *whole school*, and help to make their schools *health promoting*. In this way they will not only raise the health of the children but also raise the standards in their school.

WHAT THIS BOOK CONTAINS

This is a book of ideas and suggestions. You may wish to read it right through from cover to cover. You may wish to use it in different ways at different times. Not all schools will be able to do all the things but nearly every school or group of schools will be able to use it in some way. Here are some of the questions it will help to answer:

Chapter 1 What is meant by 'comprehensive health promotion in schools'? How easy would it be for our schools to become health promoting? Would it be worth the effort?

Chapter 2 How can we decide what are the *real* health priorities worth emphasizing in our local schools? How can we fit these in with national health policies and local values? What are 'life skills' and why are they so important in health education and promotion?

Chapter 3 What might be the components of a national health education programme? When should we introduce these health ideas and actions to children? What methods can we use (especially methods which can be used with large classes and do not require additional materials)? How can we select and practise methods which help children to think and act rather than just learn and remember?

Chapter 4 How can we use health facts and ideas to improve our children's performance in basic skill subjects such as languages and mathematics? How can we use many different subjects to pass on health ideas and develop ways of thinking and doing without weakening the programmes in these subjects?

Chapter 5 How can we encourage the school to be an example of good health to the community? In particular how can we improve the school environment and nutrition? How can we develop children as partners in promoting health around the school and in their families and communities, and in so doing make them more useful and more caring family and community members?

Chapter 6 How can we enable the school to work with the local health services to prevent ill health, identify problems early and support the physical, mental and emotional needs of children so as to promote both better health and better education in school?

Chapter 7 How could we start and organize a small and manageable project to make some of our schools into 'health action schools'? How can we plan effective programmes at the level of the single school? How can we increase numbers of 'health-promoting schools' without losing quality?

Chapter 8 How can we train our project workers, heads and teachers in school, using available resources?

Chapter 9 How can we evaluate to see whether we are making schools healthier and whether we are doing so in an efficient way? (**A simple checklist is included in this chapter.**)

Chapter 10 What simple resources are available to us (including this book and *Children for Health*) and how can we make best use of them?

There is an appendix containing some of the most important health information that all schools need to pass on.

We hope you will find this book useful. We can revise it in the light of our experience and your reactions, so please write and tell us how we could make it better.

TWO DEFINITIONS
School health promotion

School health promotion includes all the means a school uses to become healthier and to spread health to those who attend and work in it and to their families and communities.

Health promotion can sometimes come from outside, often from health workers, but more often it comes from inside the school itself through the head, the teachers, the other personnel working in the school, the children and their parents. Effective health promotion is often seen to have five components:

1. A safe and healthy school environment;
2. Sound nutrition practices;
3. Good health services in and for the school (including mental and emotional assessment and support);
4. Effective health education for children and teachers;
5. Joint health action between the school and the community.

School health education

Health education is a cornerstone of health promotion. It plays an essential role as one of the components of school health promotion and it also serves as an important part of each of the other components.

School health education is delivered by health instruction in the classroom and on the playing field through the medium of all school subjects. From the classroom it is translated into health action, around the school and through the community.

Since education is mainly acquired through participation and example, it is closely linked with the other four aspects of school health promotion. As school members observe and take part in the improvement of their environment, their nutrition and their health services, so these improve their education.

IDEAS FOR

 ## POLICY MAKERS

- Why definitions of health need to be broadened.
- How a wider definition of health can affect educational policy.
- Why school health is a worthwhile investment.
- Why school health promotion is vital to improving community health.
- Communication between national and school levels, and between education and health, is necessary for an effective policy of school health promotion.

 ## PROGRAMME DESIGNERS

- A 'whole school' approach to health. What this means for planning.
- Health as an equal entitlement of all children, boys and girls alike.
- Implications for programmes.
- Giving children the life skills to make wise decisions and act on them.
- Widening programme planning to link schools with homes and communities. Helping the children at home to become fit for school.

 ## LOCAL PLANNERS, MANAGERS AND TRAINERS

- Health knowledge and skills are responsibilities for *all* teachers. What this means for project planning and training.

 ## HEADS, TEACHERS AND LOCAL HEALTH WORKERS

- How effective health promotion can make schools happier and improve academic results.
- Children need to be seen as partners in health promotion.
- School health programmes involving five components: health teaching in class; health across the curriculum; action for a healthy school; health action between schools and community; and health services provided by the school.

CHAPTER 1

Comprehensive School Health Promotion

• What we mean by health • Why health in schools is important
• Health-promoting schools and pupils • How active health
programmes in schools help to develop active citizens who can
influence their families and communities • The five main
components of good school health programmes • How policy makers
can introduce, design and plan health programmes

What do we mean by 'health'?

Some people still believe that health and health
education are mainly matters of keeping clean
and not becoming ill. The World Health
Organization reminds us that the idea of health
is something far wider than hygiene or the
'absence of disease'.

It involves *physical health:*
feeling fit and well.

It involves *mental and emotional health.* We need
to be happy and well balanced, and able to use our
minds efficiently as well as our bodies.

It involves *social health* as well as individual
health. Children as well as adults need
to live together, cooperate with
each other, respect each other and learn that girls
and boys always need to have equal rights and
opportunities.

It involves maintaining a *healthy environment.*
If our environment is destroyed or polluted, then
the food we eat, the water
we drink, and the air we
breathe are threatened. Our health suffers.

There are many ways in which this wider
understanding about health affects the way we
plan teaching and learning and the way we
manage the schools. Throughout this book we
shall see how taking a wider view of health
helps to make our schools not only healthier, but happier places which
produce higher academic performance.

The school and its community

A school is not just a set of buildings and their surroundings. It also comprises the children who learn in those buildings, the head and the teachers, the workers, cooks and food-sellers who work in and for the school, and the health and community workers who visit and advise the school. All these are partners in promoting health, as also are the parents of the children and the community in which the school serves.

Remember: Every teacher, every pupil, every parent is in some way a health worker. Spreading better health is everybody's concern.

Why health in schools is important

School health promotion is an investment in our future societies Here are the reasons.

• We owe it to our children that they should be as healthy and happy as possible. Good health contributes to a happy childhood.

• School children study better and are happier in school if they are fit and well.

Which is most likely to do well?

School children who are ill miss school often and find it difficult to catch up when they return to class. Sometimes they drop out of school.

School children who are not properly fit or well when they are present in school cannot concentrate on their lessons and fall behind in their class work.

Children who are unhappy or frightened cannot set their minds to their studies.

• School children are part of a family. They are often able to spread good health messages and good health practice from school to home.

They have a special role to play helping their younger sisters and brothers become healthy and happy. Through talking and playing with these younger children they help them become ready to learn well at school when they get there.

Tomorrow's parents

• School children are tomorrow's parents. If they learn and practise good health knowledge and skills *now* and develop caring attitudes *now* they are likely to carry these forward to the next generation.

Children who are taught to observe, to listen, to communicate, to take decisions about their own health and about the health of others become not only good parents but active and useful community members.

The nature of health promotion in schools

If we consider how we can best improve the health of our communities, we realize how important the school is in meeting these goals. The Ottawa Charter for Health Promotion (1986) states that *health is created by people in the places in which they live*. People become healthier by caring for themselves and others, by taking wise decisions which affect their lives, and by influencing the society around them to create circumstances which allow members to attain good health. All these qualities can be promoted by schools.

Schools can help young people to acquire the basic skills to create health. These are sometimes called *life skills* and are described in Chapter 2. They include decision-making, problem-solving and communication. When people have such skills they are more likely to adopt a healthy lifestyle.

Schools that promote health and help spread ideas and practices to the community help the whole of that community.

A SCHOOL THAT PROMOTES HEALTH THEREFORE

- is *all for health*, fostering it with every means at its disposal;
- *involves all school and community members* in efforts to promote health;
- strives to set an *example* through environment, nutrition, safety, sports and recreations as well as by the way it educates children and spreads activities beyond the classroom and into the community;
- *takes action* to improve the health, mental and emotional as well as physical, of the whole school community (see page 99);
- *develops life skills* in children and promotes ways of giving them responsibility, raising their self-esteem and recognizing their efforts and achievements.

Prevention: a key to health promotion

One of the most important aspects of health in schools is to help children to learn how to *prevent* ill health.

- Children need to learn and *practise* good health habits, good hygiene and good safety codes. This involves learning to take responsibility and learning to take decisions.
- They need to *learn how to look ahead* so that they understand the consequences of unhealthy actions, especially those (like not taking care of teeth) which do not seem to have any immediate bad effects.
- They need to understand that our health is closely linked to the health of others and why, therefore, it is important for them to help spread good health ideas to their friends, to younger children, and also to children who have not been able to go to school.

None of these ideas and actions are easy for children. Indeed, we are often asking them to do things which most adults cannot or will not do. There are many poor health examples for children to copy. There are many pressures on children to act in unhealthy ways. There are many people who do not want children to make up their own minds. Children in school need all the help and support they can get. That is why *all* heads and *all* teachers have a health responsibility towards their children.

Many bad examples and influences

Health-promoting pupils and the Child-to-Child ideas

Child-to-Child and *Children for Health*

One essential component of a health-promoting school is that it should have health-promoting pupils. Over the last fifteen years the Child-to-Child movement has encouraged schools to look upon children as partners in health promotion and to recognize the particular role they can play. This is outlined in some detail in *Children for Health* produced by Child-to-Child in association with UNICEF and recommended to be used alongside this book.

The key message from the Child-to-Child movement is that children are an exceptionally powerful force in health promotion. They are the one asset that every school, however poor, has at its disposal. But in order to be effective they need to be respected and encouraged to think and plan for themselves. That is why the development of life skills is so very important. But we should never forget that children are not little adults. They need to be interested and to enjoy the activities they do. They should not be asked to undertake tasks which are not appropriate for them to do, or those which adults do not want to do.

One key to choosing good activities and to giving the children the power to think and act is to use a methodology which encourages them to do so and which links their school learning with their home lives. This active methodology is discussed in Chapter 3.

Rights and responsibilities

Active schools form active citizens

Every citizen has a right to basic health knowledge and health care but also a duty actively to help others maintain and improve their health. Children are citizens and have rights and duties in just the same way as adults. In many countries nearly half the citizens are children. If we promote health in schools in a way which encourages children to think actively, take positive health action and cooperate together in helping one other become healthier, we are promoting active citizenship.

All citizens –
All Health Workers

Girl and boy citizens have equal rights and responsibilities

Sometimes we think that some health actions are more suited to one gender than another. This is usually not correct. One of the most important roles of a health-promoting school is to convince all its members (the teachers as well as the children) that both sexes have equal responsibilities in health; that fathers and older brothers need to care for the health and development of younger children just as keenly and actively as mothers and elder sisters.

When girls and boys work together to take action for health they can show adults how effective such cooperation can be. The ideas and experience gained in school can help children when they become parents.

The five components of a health programme in schools

Every school needs, therefore, to have the following five components in its programme.

Basic health instruction

Children need to learn specific health facts and ideas to understand them and the ideas behind them. This implies that there is a planned programme to teach these ideas and the time available to do it. Children also need to be taught through a methodology which develops life skills. (These are discussed in Chapters 2 and 3.)

Health ideas and skills reinforced across the curriculum

Since every teacher is a teacher of health (and since many teachers at primary level teach a whole class and not separate subjects) they can introduce examples and activities connected to health in much of their teaching. This helps children understand the health messages better and makes subjects like reading or maths or art more real, more interesting and more active by linking them with topics which are interesting and important to children. (This is discussed in Chapter 4.)

Good health practised around the school

This involves planning to make the school a safe and healthy place, providing a clean environment and the best possible nutrition for the children. All who work in the school have a role to play in helping to achieve these goals. This would imply a set of school health rules and active health responsibilities for teachers and children. Local communities also have responsibilities in the provision of facilities for schools. Local government bodies need to be aware of these responsibilities.

Health knowledge and skills spread to the community

These involve active community participation in school health promotion and the transfer of knowledge from school to community. This is where the involvement of children using effective Child-to-Child approaches becomes so important. (This is discussed in Chapters 3 and 5.)

Schools health services

These involve establishing the closest possible links with health workers so that *together* they can:

● take action to *prevent* ill health and unhappiness in children and their families and ensure that there is no discrimination either between sexes or according to belief or social class;

● help to monitor the health (including hygiene and nutrition) of children and the school as a whole;

● give expert help to teachers and children so that they can treat simple conditions and can choose, teach, and pass on correct messages;

● treat or refer children who are unwell, undernourished, or disabled, or who have learning difficulties, or who suffer from accidents or abuse;

● give help and support to children in school who have long-term problems with their health or in their homes. (This is discussed in Chapter 6.)

Planning health programmes

Planning health promotion and health education will only succeed if it is done in partnership between levels and between sectors.

National governments have health priorities for their children, and health policies for their schools. The national school programme always includes much health content (although it is not always in a separate health syllabus). In some countries there is an agreed 'entitlement' which lays down what every child leaving school should know and be able to do, what health standards a school should maintain and what simple health services every school has a right to expect.

Local areas also have their own priorities. Cities and rural areas, highlands and lowlands, wealthier and poorer places have different needs and problems.

Schools also have their own set of priorities (discussed in our next chapter). It is vital for schools to work within national health priorities and for national planners to recognize that schools and local areas are different and need encouragement to make their own plans.

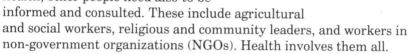

This needs a four-way communication between TOP and BOTTOM, and between EDUCATION and HEALTH.

But because health includes much more than just physical health, other people need also to be informed and consulted. These include agricultural and social workers, religious and community leaders, and workers in non-government organizations (NGOs). Health involves them all.

Let us look more closely at those who make decisions at the 'top'. In later chapters we will look at decision-making at local level.

Policy makers need to:

● **Find out what different programmes are already taking place that affect schools** (in ministries of education and of health; through voluntary agencies, including religious bodies, and by overseas aid programmes). Many of these will not know about one another. Many of the programmes may overlap. They need to be brought together so that as far as possible each will need to know what the others are doing. *Some pattern of cooperation and responsibility will need to be agreed, especially between education and health sectors.* This will not be easy.

● **Find out what is already recommended both in the teaching syllabus and in regulations for the school.**

Very often health content has been included in many different school subjects, such as health, science, home science, moral and religious education, and social studies. Sometimes textbooks in languages include health content. Often many useful topics will be covered but often some vital ones are omitted and there are many overlaps.

Often there are good health regulations, but here too they may be found in separate documents – some about *disease prevention*, sometimes even referring to special conditions such as HIV/AIDS or immunization; some about *screening* (that is, checking the height, weight and health of children); some about *school feeding*, nutrition and the planting of gardens; some about *school hygiene* and water supplies; some about *safety*; and some about *discipline*. The advice will vary from that which is necessary in all schools to that which is possible only in schools which are richer and more accessible. The policy makers need to sift what is necessary and achievable from what is desirable and often impracticable.

- **Decide and agree an 'entitlement'** (or, at least, a set of *expectations*).
  - What knowledge and health skills can we expect *all* children who have had basic education to possess?
  - What attitudes and practices could we expect *all* schools to develop in teachers and children?
  - What minimum health provisions should we expect *all* schools to make?
- **Decide and agree recommended approaches to health in schools**, e.g.
  - involvement of all teachers
  - close links with health workers
  - health committees involving community members
  - encouragement of certain methodologies (which promote active thinking and lead to health action)
  - encouragement of children as health promoters.
- **Discuss and agree what responsibilities local areas and schools should have** to make their *own* health plans within national guidelines, to meet their own special priorities.
- **Find out what resources will be needed to make change happen**. A small number of books and materials may be necessary for teachers (see Chapter 9) but the most important resource is the knowledge and skill of teachers (see Chapter 8).
- **Decide how the new approaches to health promotion can be implemented** gradually and realistically without causing bad feeling and asking people to do too much too soon.
- **Decide how changes can be monitored and measured**. This usually means looking at what is happening *now* and so that it will be possible to compare it with what has happened after some time (perhaps a year, perhaps two years, perhaps five years on).

REMEMBER

Build on what already happens (A lot more than you think)

Get people talking and working together
(Share good ideas don't keep them hidden)

Don't make demands which are very difficult for schools to meet
Always keep poorer schools in mind.

Build on success
Some schools will take up the ideas quicker than others. Praise these rather than blaming others. Get them to share their success.

Trust teachers, children and communities and praise their achievements
With confidence and enthusiasm they can move mountains.

Do not expect many changes too quickly

QUESTIONS FOR EVERYONE

Can we afford to neglect health education in our schools?

Look, we've done really well

- Does poor health affect our school attendance, and increase 'drop outs'?
- Could improved health programmes result in happier children who would work more effectively and get better exam results?

Do we need a whole health plan for the whole school?

- Are we happy about our own definitions of health (are they too narrow)? Do we make sufficient links between hygiene, disease management, mental, social and environmental health?
- Do we have a well thought out health policy in our schools which links different aspects of health such as classroom teaching, nutrition, safety, school hygiene and sanitation? If not might one be made?

Have you done the homework I set you on healthy lifestyles?

How far is our programme helping to produce active citizens to promote better health?

- Do *all* teachers see themselves as having a responsibility for improving the health of the school and are they aware of the examples they are setting?
- Could we be giving our children more initiative and responsibility?
- Are we recommending and using methods which develop life skills and encourage children to think actively and to link health learning with health action?
- Should we become more concerned about the health and development of our future pupils (the little brothers and sisters of children already in school)? What could we do?

How well are we communicating together?

- How well do we link in with people who organize health education at national level?
- Are health and education workers working together in our area?

IDEAS FOR

 ## POLICY MAKERS

- Health promotion is based on two sets of priorities: health priorities and life-skills priorities.

- Choosing necessary content for *all* children taught in a way which develops active thinkers.

 ## PROGRAMME DESIGNERS

- How to identify and choose priorities. Six key themes identified including all the 'prime messages' listed in *Children for Health*.

- The need to make provision for both national and local health priorities.

- How to match priorities and ways of teaching about them to the age and interests of children.

- The meaning of the term 'life skills' and why they are so important in health programmes.

- What kind of objectives to set at different levels.

 ## LOCAL PLANNERS, MANAGERS AND TRAINERS

- Identifying local needs and priorities and linking them with national priorities.

- Different kinds of local priorities and reasons for choosing them.

 ## SCHOOL AND COMMUNITY

- Linking national objectives with 'our objectives'.

- Life-skills approaches are possible for all teachers (even those with little training).

CHAPTER 2

Choosing Content that Really Matters

● Health priorities and life skills – essential content in health programmes ● What health priorities are and how they need to be chosen ● National and local health priorities ● Matching content to the needs and interests of children of different ages ● What life skills need to be taught; how these are linked to the development of attitudes ● The importance of cultural beliefs and values in choosing content ● Choosing and writing objectives at different levels

Which facts and skills are most important to teach?

Health priorities

Nobody in the world knows all there is to know about health. We need to select what we want children to learn at every level. We also need to make a distinction between what is *useful* for children know and what is *really necessary* for them to know and do. School syllabuses in every country contain some health content, but some topics are repeated unnecessarily in different subjects. Some necessary content is left out. Syllabuses are crowded, so we need to be sure that we emphasize those contents which are *absolutely necessary* for all schools to teach and all children to learn.

Ways of learning, thinking and behaving.

Knowing *about* health priorities is only half of what is needed. We need to transfer that knowing into *active thinking and action for health*. The term 'life skills' is often used to describe such thinking and action and we shall be looking at life skills later in the chapter. Both health messages and life skills depend on *attitude change*. In order improve our own health, to take decisions, to pass on messages, to help others we must *want* to change, *feel a need* to help others, *feel pride* in being healthy, *be open-minded* to change. Promoting such attitudes is the most important (and most difficult) task for health education. Attitudes are based on *values* which we hold. Some of these values are universal, all societies in the world share them. Some relate to particular societies and particular beliefs. It is important for all of us to be clear what our values are.

Health priorities

Health priorities are chosen because the knowledge and actions based on them have a really important effect on the lives of people and their communities. Some health priorities relate mainly to school children themselves. Some relate to their families and particularly to their younger brothers and sisters. Many of the most important health priorities are the same for most countries in the world. A great number of these are listed in a very clear and useful book produced by UNICEF called *Facts for Life*. It divides health priorities into sections. In each section there are a number of key messages which UNICEF and WHO believe 'every citizen has a right to know'.

There is a companion volume entitled *Children for Health*. This book contains all the health information contained in *Facts for Life* and links this with action which children can take to understand and act upon these messages[1]. There are twelve sections. Each section has about five or six key messages. **These key messages are listed in the appendix of this book**.

In addition to the priorities included in *Children for Health* there are some others which are equally important, especially in the later years of basic education. Our list includes six themes including all the key messages contained in *Children for Health*. It is based on content identified by health educators working in the Ministry of Education in Ghana.

PRIORITY HEALTH THEMES

Hygiene and sanitation
- Personal hygiene including care of body, teeth, skin
- Community hygiene (including environmental protection)
- Diarrhoea, prevention and management
- Worms and parasites

Nutrition
- Good food and nutrition practices
- Breastfeeding
- Food hygiene and safety

Growth and development
- Growth and development (mind and body) of babies and young children
- Growing and changing through puberty, including sexual awareness
- Safe motherhood / timing births   *continued* →

---

[1] We recommend that *Children for Health* be used as a companion volume to this book, whenever possible.

Serious communicable diseases
- Immunization against 'killer diseases' of babies and young children
- Insect-borne diseases (especially Malaria)
- Coughs; colds; pneumonia; tuberculosis

Safety and safe lifestyles
- Prevention of AIDS and STDs
- Preventing accidents including home and road safety and first aid.
- Prevention of substance abuse (to include addiction to alcohol and tobacco, and the safe use of medicines)

Recognizing and helping the disabled

Other countries may have separate lists but they are likely to contain a similar number of themes.

Teaching and learning takes time if we are to develop real understanding leading to better health.
The total number of priority messages is not very large and all can easily be taught to, and learnt by, children in the first eight or nine years of school education. But although the number of messages to be taught and learnt is quite small it takes time to for children to understand the message, practise skills and realize what action needs to be taken. That is why it is very important to concentrate on a few key themes and messages rather than half-learning a larger number.

National priorities and local priorities

Most of the topics listed earlier and in *Children for Health* will be relevant to all countries, especially those in Asia, Africa and Latin America. Many countries have listed their own **national priorities** and some have their own versions of *Facts for Life* or *Children for Health* in local languages. Make sure you know what these are.

In addition there will be **local priorities**.

These may relate to **local social conditions**, e.g. overcrowding in towns; road accidents near highways; tensions and bad feelings between communities (social health); environmental pollution.

Priority: road safety

Priorities: guinea worm; bilharzia

There may be **local customs or beliefs** which are damaging to health, e.g. stopping breastfeeding suddenly; wrapping up children with fever in blankets; putting cow dung on cuts and wounds; giving pills or other medicines rather than liquid to children with diarrhoea; allowing very young girls to marry and have children … there are many more.

There may be **local diseases or parasites** which cause diseases, e.g. guinea worm; bilharzia; dengue fever; scabies; river blindness.

Understanding local priorities

Local priorities are particularly important for another reason. Because they matter a great deal to families and communities everyone wants to see them taught and this builds links between schools, health workers and communities. Not all heads, teachers or health workers come from the same communities in which they work. It is vital, therefore, for them to find out local beliefs and practices, and what the local community feels to be really important.

Different ages, different priorities

Lower primary

Not all these health themes need to be taught to all children from the beginning of the school. For younger children three categories are most important: HYGIENE, SAFETY and GOOD FOOD.

Middle primary

As children come into the middle classes of school other themes and topics can be added each year, taking care not to overload the programme and to allow plenty of time for children really to understand the priorities. Topics such as Malaria, Worms, Immunization and Helping the Disabled are very suitable for this age.

Upper primary and junior secondary

In many countries most children (often more girls than boys) leave school at the end of a period of basic education (usually six, seven, eight or nine, or even ten years). There are some topics which are very important to emphasize before they leave. These are those which affect their own growth and development, their lifestyles and their future roles as mothers and fathers (*remember these topics are just as important for boys as they are for girls*). Always remember that children in the 12-15 age group do not want adults to 'preach' to them. It is important to find out from children how *they* view the problem and what *they* feel a need to know. Then you may able to present priorities as 'knowledge you will find useful' or better still 'messages you can pass on to others'.

Same theme, different approaches

Content needs to be approached in different ways as children grow older. Children have different characteristics and interests at different ages. Below we take one component of the theme Safety, the prevention of accidents. We examine how it can be broken down into topics which are suitable for particular age groups.

Characteristics of lower-primary children: 6-8

• Like active approaches such as games, songs and dances.

• Are very imaginative; love stories and puppet plays.

• Like following rules and being helpful.

• Do not understand abstract ideas such as 'health' or 'pollution' or 'conservation'. (They must be introduced at this level through activities).

EXAMPLES OF TOPICS AND ACTIVITIES RELATED TO THE THEME 'SAFETY'

Topics

▪ Preventing accidents and keeping myself safe at home and school.

▪ Keeping safe on the road.

▪ What to do when an accident happens.

Activities

▪ Listening to a story about home accidents.

▪ Follow up with drama and drawing.

▪ Learning safety rhymes and songs (older children can teach and test these).

▪ Learning road safety drills, practically, on a 'road' marked out on the school playground.

Characteristics of middle-primary children: 9-11

• Still like 'fun' activities and are physically very active.

• Are very helpful and like being given particular responsibilities.

• Can work together well with others provided they are given tasks they understand.

• Are community minded and like taking action in home and in the neighbourhood.

• Like remembering facts and being quizzed on them.

• Like watching and taking part in practical demonstrations (they still find abstract ideas difficult to understand).

• Need help and support planning and doing new things on their own (especially outside the school).

Characteristics of upper primary and junior secondary children: 12-15

• Like to know 'why' they are being asked to do things'.

• Are interested in solving problems.

• Are very interested in their own development (since they are beginning to experience puberty).

• Like to be given responsibility and being trusted to carry things through (though they do not always do so).

• Can understand abstract ideas and like discussing them.

• Resent being 'talked down to' by adults.

Learning and life skills

When children learn about health they learn far more than facts. They also learn what are called 'skills' which help them learn better and apply what they have learnt to real life not only right now but also after they have left schools and become adults. Sometimes these are called 'life skills'. Life skills can be practical, like knowing how to use first aid, and they can be ways of thinking about how to find out or solve problems. They can also be ways of communicating, feeling and behaving, such as knowing how to work together with others.

Life skills are also very closely linked to the development of good attitudes. One of the most important life skills is the skill of listening to people; if you listen to them you are showing them respect (an attitude).

LIFE SKILLS WE NEED TO DEVELOP THROUGH HEALTH EDUCATION

Practical skills
- Doing skills, e.g. Weighing and measuring young children.
- Making a water filter.
- Organizing skills, e.g. Making a household budget.
- Recording skills, e.g. Mapping and describing water sources.

Thinking skills
- Problem-solving, e.g. Why our water at home is not safe to drink?
- Decision-making, e.g. What to do to make it safer?
- Critical thinking, e.g. What are the hidden messages in an advertisement?
- Creative thinking, e.g. What games can I invent to help my little brother learn how to count?

Skills for communicating and behaving
- Communication, e.g. How can I ask adults about changes in my body now I am twelve years old?
- Listening, e.g. What is the three-year-old trying to tell me about why she is frightened?
- Developing empathy ('getting inside others and understanding how they feel'), e.g. What does it feel like to be blind?
- Resisting pressures, e.g. How can I say 'no' to smoking and still keep my friends?
- Relations with others, e.g. How can I work together with other children on the road safety campaign, and respect their ideas?
- Self-awareness, e.g. How can I learn to criticize my own health habits?
- Coping with stress and emotions, e.g. How can I concentrate on preparing for my exams now that my father is so ill?

We learn these life skills by using them. That is why the way we teach and learn (described in our next chapter) is just as important as the messages we select.

What are the 'hidden messages' in this advertisement

Life skills and attitudes

Life skills depend on attitudes. Four attitudes above all others need to be developed through health education in schools:

- Self-respect
  I want to be clean, fit and healthy.
- Self-esteem
  I know I can make a difference to the health of my family even though I am still a child.
- Respect for others
  I need to listen to others, to respect them and their customs even when I find I cannot agree with them.
- Concern for others
  I want to do my best to help others to become healthier especially those who particularly need my help.

Our values and how they are related to our cultures

Attitudes are based on values, the guidelines people set up to tell us what is right and wrong, good or bad. A value has been described as *something which promotes behaviour which is beneficial (good) for the person who practises it and also for those on whom it is practised*. Some values are the same worldwide. They include values such as *honesty, loyalty, dependability, respect for others* and *making peace.*

Other values are linked more closely to different cultures and beliefs. These are of different kinds. Every culture contains traditional beliefs and customs and values which promote positive behaviour and lead towards good health but in other cases our health knowledge will tell us that the traditional value can be proved to have a *bad effect on 'those on whom it is practised'.* **Very often such beliefs affect the health and development of girls.**

> **Examples of beliefs and customs which promote health and happiness:**
> - Respect for old persons in the community
> - Prohibiting sex with mothers for some time after birth
> - Grandparents telling stories to young children
>
> **Examples of beliefs and customs which harm health:**
> - Early marriage and pregnancy
> - Female circumcision
> - Girls or children eating after men have finished
> - Throwing away colostrum (the 'first milk') of mothers

School children will often be faced with values which conflict. Moreover they will also find that adults say one thing and do another. There are no easy answers, no ready advice we can give to children who are faced with the painful task of making up their minds about values. All we can say is that they need time to discuss these conflicts and that teachers and other adults must be prepared to listen and talk to them to help them make choices. At school, *role play* is a helpful way of helping children to face and talk about values which conflict.

Cases and choices

Joe is fifteen and now interested in girls. Many of his friends have already had sex and have begun teasing him because he hasn't. His older brother, who he admires, has a succession of attractive girl friends. His teacher preaches the dangers of AIDS and recommends the children wait until they have 'one steady partner', but the teacher is known to be interested in a girl from one of the upper classes. The Reverend John, his clergyman and relative, who Joe also likes, urges him to wait until he gets married. He has a book which tells him that condoms give protection but doesn't know what to do or who to ask for more information.

Sita is intelligent, and does extremely well in school, better than any of the boys in her year. She has learnt about nutrition and the importance of eating the right kind of foods, especially during pregnancy. Her mother, who *is* pregnant, looks tired and ill, works too much and eats too little. At meal times she holds back from eating so that she can offer all the best food to her husband, his brother and their sons. She urges Sita to do the same saying that is the way women must act. Her father, who she loves, expects this; and her brother, who is studying biology in the top class of his secondary school, just laughs when she tries to ask him what she should do.

Objectives for health education programmes

When we are planning programmes for health education either at central level or in schools we need to have objectives. They help us in two ways. First they help us to be clear in our minds about what the most important ways are in which we want the children to develop (through learning more and doing more). Second, unless we have objectives we cannot find out whether changes have taken place because we will not know what to measure. We always make objectives at different levels. We will need **general** objectives for health education which are linked with everything we plan and do. We will need objectives for each important **theme or unit** (such as Nutrition, Safety, or Substance Abuse). Finally we shall need more detailed objectives for **topics** (such as Care of Teeth, Smoking, or Cholera).

Level 1: General objectives

These are the objectives which we need to remember *every time* we present health in the classroom and *all the time* we encourage children to take action around the school and in the community. They will include those life skills and attitudes and values which we mentioned earlier. Here are some general objectives which have been based on those agreed for the School Health Action Programme developed from Kenyatta University in Kenya.

GENERAL OBJECTIVES FOR ALL LEARNERS

By the end of the first cycle of basic education all children should be able to:

1. Accept responsibilities within the limits of age, ability and place in the family and community for:

▪ the maintenance and improvement of their own health;

▪ the maintenance and improvement of the health of others, especially other children to whom they can communicate health knowledge, skills and attitudes.

2. Realize what they are able to do in the school and home and also when and how they need to refer problems to adult members of their families, to their teachers and to health workers.

3. Acquire an understanding of the meaning of 'good health', realizing that it includes healthy minds, emotions and relationships in additions to healthy bodies.

4. Realize that the health of the individual is closely linked with the maintenance of a clean, safe and well-managed environment. Develop attitudes to conserve and improve environments.

---

5. Appreciate that there is a minimum body of health knowledge and skills which *every citizen, including every child,* has a right to know and a duty to pass on to others. Develop a desire to acquire such knowledge and skills and the ability to communicate them to others.

6. Appreciate that the ability to help others depends on a capacity to listen and understand them. This in turn is based on attitudes of respect for others and their points of view.

7. Appreciate that many conditions which cause ill health can be prevented by good health practices and that ill health is often not a matter of ill luck and seldom the result of ill will of others.

8. Appreciate that good health for self and others depends not only on acquiring knowledge and learning good practices but also depends on the ability and confidence to take sensible decisions in new situations. Develop the capacity to make such decisions and to resist pressures to do what they know to be wrong.

9. Examine traditional customs and beliefs as they relate to health practices and issues, and form judgements as to which may be beneficial and which harmful.

Level 2: Objectives for a health theme

Alongside these general objectives we need to set out the objectives for each theme. Here are the objectives for one of the sections under the theme Nutrition from the Ghana programme described earlier.

GOOD FOOD AND NUTRITION PRACTICES

Children should

KNOW:

1. That all children need good food to grow and study well.

2. The different types of food available and affordable within their homes and communities; why we need different kinds of food to help in different ways (growth, energy, protection); and therefore why we need to eat a variety of food.

3. Which foods in our communities are of these different types and provide good nutrition at lowest cost.

continued →

4. What kinds of beliefs and customs are associated with food, including feeding babies.

5. The importance of growing, collecting and eating fruit and green leafy vegetables as these provide vitamin A which protects our bodies and particularly our eyesight.

6. The importance of frequent feeding, especially in very young children, since their stomachs are very small (yet they need plenty of food).

7. The importance of eating before school so that they have energy to learn well.

8. That girls need as much nutrition as boys and that practices within families must promote good nutrition of girls and women.

9. How to recognize the signs of poor feeding and malnutrition in children in their communities.

Children should

DO:

1. Eat as effectively as they can given local customs and food available.

2. Prepare the best meals possible given responsibilities and food available.

3. Ensure that so far as possible any small children they look after eat four or five times a day.

4. Develop skills in growing and tending vegetables.

5. Cooperate to demonstrate messages of good nutrition to their communities (e.g. through songs and plays) .

Children should be able to

FEEL:

1. Responsibility for getting the best nutrition available so that they can study well and be effective family members.

2. Concern that their younger brothers and sisters have the best nutrition available.

3. Pride in good food customs and concern for those which have a bad effect on health.

4. Desire to spread good nutrition messages through their communities in ways which are most acceptable given existing traditions and customs.

5. Concern for other children in the community who are too thin.

(See *Children for Health*, pages 62-71 and 172-181.)

Level 3: Objectives for a topic

Themes will be divided into topics. Each topic will contain a number of activities to help the learner to *understand* the ideas and to link understanding with *action*. This involves different steps which we describe in our next chapter. The objectives of a topic will include what children should know and be able to do at the end of a unit; but they should also set out what activities the children should undertake. We also return to the planning of these topic objectives in Chapter 7.

Here are objectives for a topic on malnutrition (for class 5). Note that the 'knowing' and 'doing' objectives are set out in ways that are easy to measure, but that there is also a note of the methods which will be used to develop life skills and attitudes.

OBJECTIVES FOR UNIT ON MALNUTRITION (CLASS 5)

By the end of the topic children should be able to:

● *Distinguish* between different kinds of malnutrition in children.

● *List* the main causes of child malnutrition in their own communities and give some suggestions on how malnutrition should be made less.

● *Demonstrate* correctly how health workers recognize malnutrition through:

　1. The appearance of children.

　2. The use of weight charts (particularly in children under 2 years).

　3.The measurement of the arm circumference of children from 1-5 years.

● *List* the effects of malnutrition on children's lives and upon their studies.

● *State* what they may be able to do to ensure that children in their own families are not malnourished.

continued →

> **During the unit children should be given the opportunity to** *discuss* the causes of malnutrition and its links with poverty. They should be encouraged to *feel concern* for children who are malnourished and for the conditions which cause it.

QUESTIONS FOR EVERYONE

Health messages

- Have we identified minimum priority messages for our schools?
- Do our current programmes include these messages?
- If not, how can we fill the gaps?

Life skills

- Are we educating our children to take decisions and take action or are we just teaching them *about* health?

Different age, different priorities

- Are we suiting our content and methods to the age of our children?
- How can we build on their interests and enthusiasm to help them become our partners in health promotion?

Objectives and the curriculum

- Do national objectives exist?
- Would a set of national objectives be acceptable in our country . . . would it be useful?
- Could we adapt such an idea at state or local level?

IDEAS FOR

 POLICY MAKERS

- Learning needs to be viewed as linking school, home and community.

 PROGRAMME DESIGNERS

- Why a curriculum statement for health education is necessary and why it needs to contain more than a list of the contents of health periods.
- The need to emphasize a limited number of major health activities linking learning in school with action in the home.
- A four-step approach:
  - Recognize and understand
  - Study
  - Act
  - Evaluate
- The need to view activity methods as something beyond mere activity in the classroom; rather as methods which promote active thinking and doing and develop life skills.

 LOCAL PLANNERS, MANAGERS AND TRAINERS

- Need to understand how active approaches can develop learning and life skills in children and raise self-confidence.
- Need to encourage and prepare teachers to try new methods (which are less difficult than they think and make teaching more enjoyable).

 SCHOOL AND COMMUNITY

- Nine methods examined: in each of these we need to emphasize ways which encourage children to think, create, take decisions and translate such decisions into action.
- The need to link methods used with life skills that children develop. How giving children responsibility makes the teacher's task easier.

CHAPTER 3

Approaches to Learning and Teaching

Part 1: Presenting our content

● A curriculum plan for health education ● The importance of correct health facts on which to base teaching ● Steps in developing and presenting a health topic (some taking place in school, some at home and in the community) ● The real meaning of the term *active methods*

The curriculum for health education

In Chapter 1 we discussed the responsibilities of policy makers for planning health education. Now we have looked at what children should learn, let us see what we should like a national statement of policy (or national curriculum) for health education to contain. Health education is a different kind of subject from others such as mathematics or geography. Basic content must be *introduced* in special periods, sometimes in a separate subject called 'health education' but more often as a part of other subjects such as environmental science. That content then needs to be *reinforced* through other subjects in the curriculum, *demonstrated* through the life of the school and *spread* from the school to the community. A national statement might, therefore, need to look like this:

POSSIBLE TABLE OF CONTENTS FOR A 'NEW STYLE' HEALTH EDUCATION CURRICULUM

1. A joint **foreword** from directors of both education and health stating why health education in school is important and why it could raise standards in schools.

2. A statement of **general aims or objectives**. Include the life skills and attitudes which need to be developed all through the programme.

3. Health themes and topics identified: some themes, such as Hygiene, Safety and Nutrition will carry on right through every class. Other themes, such as Disease Prevention, Growth and Development, and Disability, will start a little later but then continue with new content added every year.

4. Objectives for each of these themes and topics showing what we might expect children to *know, do* and *feel* by the time they have reached different levels.

continued →

5. A programme showing how the different themes could be *introduced* and how they could be *reinforced* across the curriculum.
6. Active methodologies recommended to promote real understanding, develop life skills and attitudes, and link learning with health action at home.
7. Time made available to incorporate **local health priorities** and an invitation to schools to do so.
8. A special reference to the way that health knowledge needs to be **exemplified** by health action around the **school** and spread by teachers and children to the **community**.
9. A note on **assessment** not only of health knowledge but also of changes in health action and attitudes and the acquisition of life skills.

As we can see from the example above there may no need to introduce a new subject or to conduct a major curriculum revision before producing a statement of what the national health content should be.

But if a statement such as this is produced it can help to reduce confusion and overlap between syllabuses and make it much easier for national and local programmes to concentrate on teaching health in the best possible way.

Let us now look at some of the different parts of this curriculum in more detail.

Components of the health curriculum

When can we introduce new content?

As we have mentioned it is necessary to have special periods to present new health content. Some countries designate health education as a subject on its own. More often health content is taught in special units within certain subjects such as science, environmental science or home science. We sometimes refer to these as 'carrier subjects' because they carry the main messages. However, school programmes are crowded and no one should expect to have more than one period a week to introduce health content. *This means that we have to select the content we teach very carefully.* But even though the number of periods available to teach health content will be limited, there *are* other ways and times to reinforce those facts presented in the 'health' periods. For example:

● Messages can be taught to children in **short 'health spots'** for ten minutes each day by the class teacher or in assembly.

● In some schools, heads use **assemblies** to give children the opportunity to sing songs, read poems or perform plays containing health messages.

● Sometimes **health staff or health education workers** come to talk to the school or to individual classes. (Be sure the class teacher follows up these talks to make sure that the children have understood them well.)

● In our next chapter we will show how **other school subjects** can be used to reinforce or health topics.

Getting the health facts right

Every health theme and every topic contains important health facts. It is vital that these facts are correctly presented and learnt. Wrong facts well taught can be very dangerous. Therefore time needs to be spent making sure that these facts are learnt and understood. This is not as easy as it looks.

● Sometimes the health messages we teach are too general to be useful.

● Sometimes they are only partly right.

● Sometimes they are WRONG (because they come from that big store of wrong health information which we all grew up with).

VAGUE, HALF-RIGHT OR WRONG

'Keeping clean helps you become healthy.'

> **Too vague**: cleaning hands after using the toilet, or cleaning a baby's bottom, is far more important than washing behind your ears.

'Giving oral rehydration cures diarrhoea.'

> **Only half-right**: and therefore dangerous. Oral rehydration doesn't cure. It puts back the liquid a body loses. If we believe it 'cures', we may just give one or two doses, like medicine.

'If people have fever, wrap them up well so that they will sweat and the fever will "come out".'

> **Quite wrong**: You can kill people that way, yet this is the practice in many communities.

A health topic: one period or a series of linked activities?

Priority health messages need to be understood. After understanding comes action. When children take action they not only help others but their understanding becomes greater. They have *transformed knowledge into change of behaviour*. That is what health education must do. For this reason it is nearly always necessary to think of planning a series of activities rather than one lesson.

Children for Health suggests the following four steps* for teachers and children working through a topic – in this case diarrhoea.

TEACHER AND CHILDREN NEED TO:

Step 1 Recognize / understand

Recognize the topic to be a priority that must be studied, e.g. diarrhoea kills babies; there are ways or preventing this.

Understand the main message, e.g. what causes diarrhoea; what dehydration is; why it kills; how can we prevent it.

Step 2 Study

Find out more: what do the children know? What is the nature of the problem in the community, e.g. 'A survey: diarrhoea in our families'. How many children have had it? Are they breastfed or bottle-fed? How is it treated?

Discuss findings, e.g. which local treatments may be helpful or may be harmful?

Step 3* Act

Plan action, e.g. what can I do? What can we, the children, do together? Who can help us?
Take action myself, e.g. help baby to drink.
Take action with others, e.g. make a puppet show.

Step 4 Evaluate

Discuss action together, e.g. what did we do? Who listened to us? What improved? What didn't? What shall we do next?

*Note that the Child-to-Child resource book divides Step 3 into two steps, *Planning action* and *Taking action*. It also adds an extra step *Doing it better next time*. Thus it talks of six steps.

If we look at these steps we will notice that activities happen in different places. Sometimes they happen in the CLASSROOM or round the SCHOOL, and sometimes at HOME or in the COMMUNITY.

LEARNING AND DOING: LEARNING PLACE AND LIVING PLACE

Class/school

Home/community

Step 1

Recognize
Learning about diarrhoea and dehydration.

Step 2

Study

(1) A survey at home and with neighbours. Who suffers from it? How is it treated?

(2) Discuss findings. Which babies are most at risk? Which local remedies are helpful?

Step 3

Act
(1) Plan action (How can children help to prevent and treat diarrhoea?)

(2) Helping mother at home when the baby has diarrhoea.Washing hands after cleaning the baby's bottom. Telling 'what we learnt at school' why this is important.

(3) Making puppets and preparing our play.

(4) Performing the play in the village square.

Step 4

Evaluate
(1) 'What did we do? How well did our show work? Should we change it next time?'

(2) 'Can we remember all we learnt? Can we all make a rehydration drink?'

(3) Carrying on with actions to prevent and treat diarrhoea at home.

The length of the topics will vary. Some will be longer than others. So will the length of each step. For instance if our topic were 'Children who are disabled' our first step would be quite short. On the other hand the second step would be much longer since we would have to make a survey in the community straight away to *find out* about disabled children and then study and *discuss* what it felt like to be disabled and how we could help.

Because each topic requires a series of steps it is unlikely that schools will be able to cover more than three or four themes in each class every year. This should not worry planners or teachers. By doing a topic well children learn to think, to act and to take decisions. They are learning life skills. They are changing attitudes and reinforcing values. If teachers try to cover too much children will only learn health facts by heart and their behaviour and attitudes will not change.

What are active *methods* and what is the result of using them?

Active health education requires active methods. Many people think of active methods merely as ways of learning which are fun for children, and which help them remember their lessons better because they linked learning with doing. This is only one part of the meaning.

Active methods are also those which lead to *active thinking*, which promote real understanding of health ideas, which develop skills in planning, in taking action and in spreading health messages to others, and which help children gain life skills, develop attitudes and confirm values.

There is no question that such active methods do involve teachers in extra time and effort. Most teachers already work very hard in very difficult conditions. No one expects schools and teachers to try *all* the new methods suggested or to try them all the time. But we believe that it is well worthwhile making a start. Many schools working with the new approaches have found that as teachers, children, parents and community members learn how to work together on health activities in this way, teaching becomes easier, more cooperative and more fun. The teacher and others work *with* the children rather than *for* the children. The children become more responsible, more aware of their need to help others, better problem-solvers, better citizens.

Material resources

Although the new approaches do require additional resources few of these require additional money. Most good health education uses the resources available in the school and the community and, above all, the children themselves. In the last chapter of this book we look at ways in which schools and communities can identify, collect and use these resources.

Part 2: Active methods for learning and teaching

NINE ACTIVE METHODS FOR TEACHING AND LEARNING
ABOUT HEALTH

DISCUSSIONS	STORIES	PICTURES AND BLACKBOARD

DEMONSTRATIONS	SURVEYS	VISITS AND VISITORS

DRAMA	POEMS AND SONGS	GAMES

  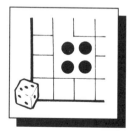

- These can be linked together with the approaches and steps described in Part 1

Nine active methods

In the second part of this chapter we shall look at nine of these methods and the ways of learning and thinking they develop. Methods will vary according to the topic and the children's ages. Few of them require much in the way of money and equipment but all of them need teachers who are willing to try new things and who are keen to help their children think for themselves.

1. Discussion groups

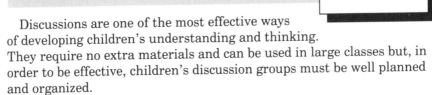

Develop skills of communication and listening; problem-solving; decision-making and critical thinking.

Discussions are one of the most effective ways of developing children's understanding and thinking. They require no extra materials and can be used in large classes but, in order to be effective, children's discussion groups must be well planned and organized.

Group size
Keep groups small so that everyone can contribute. Five to seven children is a good size. Children need to sit where they can all see each other, e.g. round a table, or on the ground. Every group needs a leader and a note-taker.

Making up rules for group work
It is important to find a way of working which does not allow one or two children to do all the thinking and talking. Sometimes children can discuss things in pairs before giving answers. This allows shy children a chance to give their ideas to bolder children. It is useful to set up 'group rules' with children before they start. If children have helped to make the rules, they will be much better at keeping to them.

Note-takers need clear instructions and simple tasks

Clarify tasks
Children may have wider problems to discuss (e.g. how can we play with our babies at home?) or narrower tasks (e.g. list four ways in which each of us can make our play area safer). In each case they should be clear about what the discussion task is, and clear about what the group has decided.

When and how to use discussion groups

Group discussions can be held when we are *studying* health topics, when we are *planning* and when we are *evaluating*. Sometimes it is possible to start a discussion by asking (and writing down) three or four important questions. Sometimes other ways can be used to help get discussions going. Here are a few:

● Starting from experience

　use stories about 'what happened to me' to start a discussion.

● Using pictures

　from books, magazines, photos, etc., e.g. a picture of a disabled child being ignored by others playing a game. 'Pretend you are the disabled child in the picture. What do you feel? How do you feel towards the other children?'

　Discuss why the children in the picture are acting in the way they are. What can be done?

● Using statements with which children opt to agree or disagree and then defend their decision.

Remember: when discussion groups are used with older children we need to choose topics which help them communicate, to listen to different points of view and to think clearly. A topic such as 'How can we help more children in our area to come for immunization' *will* **raise interesting discussion. A topic such as 'Is immunization necessary?'** *may not.*

2. Stories (... and how to make the most of them)

Stories develop our communication and listening skills, and lead on to many other activities.

Using stories is one of the best ways of introducing new health ideas, of promoting discussion and of passing on health messages to others. That is why all good health teaching makes use of stories.

Telling the stories

Choose a story which is interesting but which has a clear simple health message. Always make sure that the children can understand the language in which the story is told. Stories are usually most effective when they are told in the children's home language.

Forget you are a teacher or health worker. Just remember you are a story teller. Gather the children around you. Sometimes pictures or puppets can be used to help the telling. Sometimes songs can be used within the story. Vary your voice, loud and soft, fast and slow. Pause now and then to allow the children to think about what you are saying. Ask questions during the telling to make sure that they have understood the action so far.

Involve the children in the story right from the beginning and help them contribute to it. Here are a few suggestions:

● The children can name the characters and the story itself.

● Give them something to 'look for' in the story before you begin: 'Afterwards I want you to tell me how many children helped Peter.'

● Get them to help you build the story: 'Indira lived in a tiny house. What colour house shall we make it?' 'She had a dress just like yours, Anita, but she did not keep it as clean as you do.'

● At appropriate moments, allow them to offer opinions, and comments: 'Musa decided he was too tired to brush his teeth . . . do you think he was wise?'

● Allow them to predict the action: 'Well, he can do three things . . . what do you think he will do?'

● Invite their suggestions: 'Rani knew that the men were making the people's drinking water unsafe, but what could she do? She was only little and all alone. Who would listen to her? What do you think she could do?'

● Put them in the character's place: 'Musa didn't know what to do next. The fever kept getting worse . . . the teacher had told them what to do but he couldn't remember exactly. Can you help him?'

● When the story is over, ask them to consider alternatives: 'Suppose she had not immunized the baby, what might have happened? Would the story be different if the villagers knew what you know about mosquitoes?'

● As a variation do not finish the story. Let the children supply their own endings and discuss these.

● Finally, help the children to relate the story to their own lives: 'Has something like this ever happened to you / here? Do you know someone who . . . ? How do we do that in our village? Can we change it?'

IDEAS OF STORIES IN *CHILDREN FOR HEALTH*:

● About hygiene (page 95)

● About immunization (page 118)

● About Vitamin A (page 177)

● Also, *Child-to-child Readers* contain stories in many languages (see Chapter 10).

After the story, what next?

Stories can lead into discussions and other activities which help develop children's understanding and change their attitudes. But first *make sure that they have understood the health message.*

Here are some ways of developing deeper understanding and building new activities onto a story.
- Let a group of children tell the story, each contributing a part.
- Let them retell the story from various characters' points of view.
- Turn it into a drama and act it out.
- Help the children to draw the story in a series of pictures which they can mix up and put back in the right order.
- Make and use puppets to tell the story.
- Get the children to try out different endings or put in new characters.
- Get them to tell what happened before or after the story.
- Ask them to share the story with their friends and family.

3. Pictures and the blackboard

Pictures help to demonstrate practical skills but also develop problem-solving, and crucial thinking and understanding of other people (empathy).

Many people who use pictures use them to convey information and to make difficult things easier to understand. This is useful, but pictures can also be used as a way of posing problems and developing active and critical thinking.

Using pictures

Pictures to promote discussions:
- The picture can pose a problem directly, but it can also lead us to ask 'What went on before?' and ' What happened afterwards?'
- When pictures are shown to promote discussion, children can 'climb into a

If you saw this what would you say?

picture', taking the part of one of the people in it and answering questions such as 'What would you do if...?'
Pictures can act as a stimulus for creative work such as poems or drama.

Using pictures to test observation and critical thinking
- In lower classes pictures can be used to help children spot 'right' or 'wrong' health actions (see illustrations of accident hazards, page 168 of *Children for Health*).
- In upper classes children can learn to spot 'hidden messages' in advertisements (see the advertisement on page 28 in Chapter 2).

Pictures to test knowledge and understanding and to develop attitudes
- Which are the correct ingredients for home-made ORS?
- Which of these vegetables contain most vitamin A?
- What do you think of this?

Drawing pictures

Children can also draw pictures and make models – on their own, in pairs or (better still) in groups, or as a whole class.

Remember: Paper and colours are not always necessary. Chalk sticks, clay, leaves, flowers and seeds can make very effective class models. Children can draw on the board.

Creative use of the blackboard

For most teachers the most familiar teaching visual aid is the blackboard. Whenever possible work on the board should encourage children to think and take action rather than just to remind them of what they have learned. Here are two ideas on how to use the board to encourage active thinking.

- Build up the information on the board from ideas supplied by the children
    - *Make lists* that the children can add to. For example, when talking about foods available in the market, list them and categorize them by season and by food value.
    - *Build up pictures.* Draw outlines. Let children add in their own ideas.

You don't need to be an artist to make a drawing that gets children talking

- Use the board as a stimulus to start children's discussion
    - *Write questions*: e.g. why are some children in our neighbourhood 'too thin'?
    - *Draw pictures*: e.g. make a picture of a river with dirt floating in it. Discuss the cause and effect of actions. For example, drinking dirty water collected from the river – what would happen? Why? How could we make the river safer?

4. Experiments and demonstrations

Develop practical and observation skills, and also logical thinking.

Sometimes in explaining health ideas, health workers and teachers will need to give a demonstration such as making or mixing a rehydration drink, making a water filter, or performing first aid. But it is very difficult to learn how to do things by just watching. Children must, therefore, *make* things, *do* things, *grow* things, *weigh* things, *measure* things for themselves.

Once they understand how to do something or how to make an effective demonstration then they can show this to other children; they can incorporate the ideas into plays and puppet shows, and perform them in school and even outside it. Each time they do it correctly or explain it correctly they understand it better and are more likely to use it in their lives and homes.

FIVE EXPERIMENTS FROM *CHILDREN FOR HEALTH*

- Preparing weaning food for young babies (page 58)

- Using and interpreting growth charts (page 67)

- How latrines pollute water supplies (model, page 93)

- Explaining dehydration ('gourd baby', page 108)

- Making pendulums (to measure fast breathing, page 130)

---

5. Surveys

Develop organizing, communication, listening and problem-solving skills.

We use surveys when we are finding out more about a health issue in a community. Sometimes we are looking for things we can see or count, but more often we are finding out what people do or feel. Asking children to do a survey is a powerful way of helping them to become aware of health issues and involving them actively in learning about them.

Children can be involved at every stage: in making up the questions to be asked; in collecting the information; in making charts to show their results; and in drawing conclusions from what they have discovered.

ROAD ACCIDENT BAR CHART

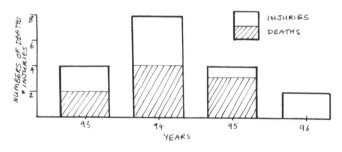

Surveys do not need to be very complicated. While the children are learning about them (and the community is getting used to the children collecting data and asking questions) keep to 'safe' topics which people will not feel sensitive about, such as accidents, hygiene, growing vegetables, toys for young children. As children gain experience they may be able to explore more sensitive topics, such as nutrition, attitudes to AIDS, or the incidence of certain diseases in a family or community.

Tact and care are needed to make sure the information collected is used to convey a health message without hurting feelings or causing embarrassment. Local culture will often determine if a topic is suitable for a survey. *Children for Health* contains a number of carefully explained examples of surveys (as well as a number of shorter examples).

SOME EXAMPLES OF SURVEYS FROM *CHILDREN FOR HEALTH*
- How do we get our water (page 91)?
- Diarrhoea in our community (page 107).
- How do we treat children who have fever (page139)?

Remember, surveys do not always need to be done in class time. If the information is easy to collect and not sensitive children can do it when they go home at night or at the weekend. But if the information is more sensitive (e.g. about alcohol, smoking or the way that illnesses are treated), then the teacher may need to help the children or even contact the parents for their permission.

6. Visits and visitors

Develops skills of observation, critical thinking and communicating well with others.

Every community has health resources worth visiting as well as people whose experience is worth sharing with children. Some visits by whole classes require much time and cost money. Since these cannot take place often, great care needs to be taken in choosing and planning them. However some visits can be arranged much more simply and some can be made by children in their own time if they are carefully thought out.

Often instead of visits, people from the community can be asked to come and talk in classes. If they wish to give a talk the teacher needs to brief them carefully, but often a better way is to invite them to answer questions. These should be prepared in advance and given to speakers well before they answer so they can think about what they are gong to say. Afterwards children can ask 'supplementary questions'.

PLACES WORTH VISITING	PEOPLE WORTH INVITING
• A dispensary or health post	• Doctors, health workers, nurses
• A dam or water works	• Local social workers
• An experimental farm	• Water workers or engineers
• A police vehicle inspection unit	• Infant and nursery teachers
• A forestry plantation	• Agricultural / veterinary / forestry officers
• A good play group or nursery school	• Police officers (road safety)
• A market or supermarket (in cities)	• Parents with their young children
• A factory (safety focus)	

Preparing with the children

It is important that children play an important part in preparing for visits and visitors. Let children write their own objectives for a visit. With them make lists of things to look for. If necessary divide them into teams, each looking at something different. For both visits and visitors prepare the questions they need to ask. Let them suggest the questions first and then modify them as necessary.

Decide in advance what kind of follow up needs to be done, e.g. pictures, models, charts, descriptions. If possible organize the class into groups to do different things which together make a whole account of the visit or talk. Here is an example based on a unit on child development. The children have observed their own babies at home, talked with mothers and visited a nursery school.

GROUP 1	GROUP 2	GROUP 3
Made a development chart for children aged 1-4 and illustrated it.	Made lists of simple toys and games for different ages and provide examples.	Wrote accounts titled 'If I were a mother how I would help my child to develop.'

7. Role playing and drama

Develops all types of communication skills, including empathy and resisting pressures.

Leads on to activities developing problem-solving and critical thinking.

Develops self-confidence.

Role play

When children pretend to be someone else or speak like someone else
they are role playing. Role
playing can be done
frequently and without
special preparation in any
health lesson. It is
particularly important
because it helps children to 'get
inside other people' and
understand how they feel and
act:

Children act as village council.

● Pretend you are a one-year-old
child crawling round the house.
How could you hurt yourself?
● (For thirteen-year-old girls)
Pretend a man you don't know who says he is a friend of your father
offers you a lift in his car. What do you do and say?
● Pretend you are very old. How would you like children to treat you?
Sometimes role playing can be more complicated. Different children can
be asked to act a number of roles in order to promote discussion.

Drama

Drama helps children understand health ideas and, at the same time,
because they are acting the part of others, it helps them respect and
appreciate what others feel. Drama teaches children to communicate.
Often children who will not talk freely in class or to adults will express
themselves in drama.

Drama can be based on stories which children have heard or read; or
on stories or health situations which are made up by the teacher or the
children themselves. Often teachers and health workers present children
with 'ready made' drama. This may not be a good idea. Children
themselves can be very imaginative and bring drama to life in a way that
adults never thought of. So whenever possible allow the children
themselves to prepare, or help to prepare the drama. If many children
are involved, divide them into smaller groups so that everyone has a
chance to think and act.

Here are some hints for working with teachers and children.

● Decide first on the health message that the drama needs to put across.

● Don't make the drama too long (the message will get muddled).

● If you are dramatizing a story think through it first (reading, telling,
discussing).

● If the story is a longer one divide it into scenes.

- Discuss what the characters are like and what they will say and do, but do not write down the words. If children have to learn the words they will not sound natural.

- Try to use some costume, however simple: a few pieces of cloth; ordinary objects like a bucket or a broom; sticks or leaves . . . are all children need.

- Always allow children to perform the drama in their own language.

Follow up from drama

After drama it is *always important to ask questions to make sure that the health message is understood*. It is very easy for children and adults to laugh at what is going on but forget why the drama was being performed. Other follow up includes:

- Discussion
  - About characters: 'Why did they act like this?'
  - About different endings: 'What would have happened if. . . ?'
  - About continuations: '. . . and what do you think happened next time?'

- Drawings, songs and poems based on the drama

- Doing it again (but better).

Mime (when children act silently)

Sometimes children can use mime and dance to put over a health message. One child can read a story or poem and others can mime it silently. Sometimes mime can be used to test children's or adult's health knowledge. For example, 'The baby is breathing like this. . .' (fast and short); 'What could be the matter?' (pneumonia).

Puppets

Children can make puppets and use them to perform health drama. Puppets are a wonderful means of developing children's powers of communication and freeing their imagination. When children 'speak through' puppets they will often say things which they would not wish or dare to say in a play. Sometimes there are traditional puppets within communities which children can use but more often they can make their own. There are many ways of doing this and none of them are difficult. Here are some examples.

Different kinds of puppets

Planning and performing drama

Remember that drama does not have to be performed for other people. Most of the time it will be done by children as part of health lessons, just to help them remember and understand better. But drama can be taken out of the classroom.

- to other classes
- in school assemblies
- to other schools (primary school children can perform for pre-schoolers)
- to parents and the community, on 'open days' and community festivals. The bigger the event the more preparation will be needed.

8. Poems and songs

Develop communication skills and imagination.

Raise interest and promote good attitudes to health.

Poems

Children are natural poets. Poetry is particularly useful in health education to describe the way that children feel about health, about the environment and about what they can do to help others. Poems can use rhymes or rhythms, but this is never necessary. Just ask the children to 'paint' their own pictures in words. Here are a just a few subjects for poems. (Let children also suggest their own.)

- *I care for my little sister* • *What do the trees tell us?* • *Our immunization soldiers* • *I have a friend (a song about the disabled)* • *Mr AIDS we'll keep you out*

Songs

Songs are always popular and effective for passing on health messages. Some are written by teachers. Sometimes professional singers and songwriters will give their services free and compose songs for children to sing. But children can also make up their own songs and set them to tunes everyone knows. They can then illustrate them with dance and mime. When children make up their own songs *make sure their health facts are correct (and that they are giving useful messages which are not too vague and general).*

9. Games

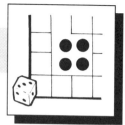

Most of us know that it is possible to make **board games** for health, like 'Snakes and Ladders', but these are often difficult to make and play in a large class. Perhaps a better method is to ask children to make their own boards and their own messages and play the games with each other. Teachers should ask children to show them the games they have made just to make sure that the messages are correct. It may even be possible to organize a competition on who can make the best board game. When children make such games they learn to draw and measure as well as understand health messages.

But many **word games** can be made using no equipment at all. They include:

● Guessing games, such as asking children to mime and guess symptoms of diseases, or the action of insect pests such as flies or mosquitoes.

● The 'What happened next?' game (after learning a health message)

The teacher starts the story: 'When Mrs Jackson bought the paraffin for the stove she poured it into a soft-drink bottle and left it on the floor. The baby was crawling round the floor. . .' Then different children (in groups or in the whole class) go on with the story, one at a time, until it ends (probably with the baby in hospital).

● The 'If I were' game. This game helps children learn to take decisions which are important for health and which they may later have to take as parents:

If I were a mother (and could choose) how many children would I have and what would be the number of years between them. Why?

If I had a baby how could I try to make sure it did well at school *from the time it was born?*

… and many others of the same kind.

Outside games

Many games can be played outside and there are many variations which can be tried out. Tag, races, hopscotch games and many others can easily be adapted to pass on health messages.

Remember:

● Children as well as teachers can make up games. Some will be new and imaginative.

● Build on and adapt games already played in the community.

● Always make sure that the health message is emphasized. (Games are such fun that the serious messages sometimes gets forgotten.)

Putting the different methods together

The table below shows how some different methods can be linked to the steps described earlier in the chapter. Some teachers will find some methods easier than others to use, and some methods will obviously be more suitable for older or younger children, but always remember:

Wherever possible choose methods which will help children think, make choices and take decisions. Do NOT underestimate children. If they are challenged and encouraged, they can do a lot more than we usually ask of them in school.

METHODS IN AND OUT OF CLASS

In class	Outside class and in home/ community

- Recognize
- Understand
  Pictures; stories; games
  Discussion groups
  Experiments and
  demonstrations

- Study (finding out more)
  Surveys; visits

- Study (discussing and recording what we have found out)
  Making graphs
  Discussion groups
  Role play
- Planning action

- Taking action (individually and together)
  Helping at home
  Drama; posters; puppets
  Taking part in campaigns
  School health action

Making plans
Making up drama
Making pictures; puppets;
posters
- Reporting and discussing
  Discussions
  Planning meetings to find out
  how to do it better next time

QUESTIONS FOR EVERYONE

A national curriculum statement for health education

• Would a statement such as that proposed at the beginning of this chapter be useful at either national or sub-national level?

• How might we set about getting one drafted?

The time available for introducing health knowledge and skills in schools

• Timetables are crowded and teachers are not superhuman. How can we, therefore, make sure that the time allocation is modest, or that the number of topics to be approached in any one class is manageable?

The approach to topic planning

• How far does the approach to topic planning (linked activities rather than single periods) make sense in our schools?

• Is the step-by-step approach possible for all topics or only some?

Methods

• Which of the methods recommended are easiest to introduce in different situations?

• Starting from local realities (class sizes; teacher training, materials available at school and at home; time; local culture), examine the methods one by one and ask when the approach *will* work and when and how it *will not*?

• In what ways do the methods we now use need to be changed

   ... to give children more responsibility?

   ... to give them more challenges to create and plan, rather than just do what we tell them?

IDEAS FOR

 ## POLICY MAKERS

• Identifying health as a cross-curricular subject involves deciding which subjects should '*carry*' the health facts and which should *reinforce* them. This has implications for planning.

 ## PROGRAMME DESIGNERS

• How health content can strengthen the educational value of other subjects, particularly through linking learning skills with life.

• Once health themes are agreed, encourage all curriculum planners to keep them in mind as they design their subject programmes.

• The need to keep health priorities in mind when designing textbooks and recommending supplementary reading.

 ## LOCAL PLANNERS, MANAGERS AND TRAINERS

• Encouraging the design and production of special cross-curriculum units to meet specially identified needs and, or, to fit in with health campaigns such as 'Road Safety Week'.

• Introducing the concept of 'health across the curriculum', both generally and as part of subject methodology in all relevant training.

 ## SCHOOL AND COMMUNITY

• Appreciating how subjects help learning in different ways and how health content can help children to apply the skills they learn to the lives they lead, e.g. measurement and health (mathematics); listening and health (language); mapping and health (social studies); conducting experiments and health (science).

• Planning health topics across subjects either over a longer period, e.g. 'Food-for-Health Term'; or over a shorter period, 'Aids Awareness Week'.

CHAPTER 4

Health Across the Curriculum

> • Why and how schools need to reinforce priority health content through all subjects in the curriculum • How using health content strengthens the teaching of different subjects • Health and science • Health and mathematics • Health and social studies • Linking subjects together around a health theme

Why or How

Once we have decided what our health priorities are and how to introduce them we need then to consider reinforcing these priorities in different subjects. Teachers can do this in different ways:

• Priority topics can be linked into teaching in all classes. Messages about personal hygiene, clean water, protecting the environment or keeping little children safe need to be stressed at every level, and so can be introduced into teaching whenever it is useful and helpful.

• In addition a health theme or topic can be selected as a month, term or year priority. Once it is introduced, the subject is then reinforced through other subjects in the curriculum.

Why we teach different subjects in different ways and why health content helps learners develop their own different ways of learning

When we introduce or reinforce health messages in other subjects we are doing far more than just using these subjects to put across health messages. Often the health content we introduce actually helps meet the needs of these subjects.

Most subjects aim to teach both **knowledge** (facts and ideas) and **skills** (how to do things and ways of thinking) and to develop particular **attitudes**. The whole school programme aims to give children a package of useful knowledge and skills which give them a firm start in life. Besides teaching different types of knowledge each different subject is particularly suitable for developing particular learning and thinking skills.

Language teaches us how to communicate and to put our thoughts in order. *Mathematics* teaches us how to be precise and logical.

Science teaches to build up evidence so that we can solve problems.

Social studies teaches us ways of understanding other people and understanding the relationship between people and the places in which they live.

Art and music help us to develop the creative talent we all have as well as how to appreciate the creativity of others.

Physical education helps us use our bodies effectively.

Moral and religious education help us learn to think more deeply about what is right and wrong.

In each case the way we learn and think is different and in each case we can use health content and health examples to help develop these ways of learning and thinking.

Most of us already use subjects such as art, craft and music to reinforce health messages. We make posters and models. We compose and perform songs and dances to help put our health messages across. But not all of us have thought about how health can help the teaching of 'examination subjects' and how they, in turn, can present and reinforce health ideas and health skills.

In this chapter we look at four subjects, science, mathematics, social studies and language. Let us start with science because it is the subject in which we often introduce health content.

Health and science

Many science lessons (such as learning about air and water, or learning about how our bodies work) are related to our health. Also the ways of learning and thinking, which science helps to develop, are important for us if we are to learn to become healthier.

Let us look at some of these ways

Students of science OBSERVE and RECORD.

They see what really is, not what they want to see.
E.g. *We observed the plants growing in two plots. We recorded their growth.*

They MEASURE and MAKE COMPARISONS.
E.g. *The plants had different spaces between them. They are of different heights . Those in one plot are taller and healthier than in the other. Those which are planted closer together are shorter and weaker than those which are planted farther apart.*

They ASK QUESTIONS; HYPOTHESIZE and PREDICT.
E.g. *Why are these differences happening? I think it may have something to do with the distance between the plants. I predict that if we plant them further apart they will grow better.*

They MAKE EXPERIMENTS and INTERPRET RESULTS.
E.g. *I tried planting seeds in the two plots at the same distance apart. When the plants came up I observed that they were much closer in size but one plot still had better growth than another. I decided that the distance apart certainly had something to do with it, but that there was something else that affected their growth.*

Then they ASK MORE QUESTIONS.
E.g. *So I asked myself, 'What is this something else?' and decided to ...*

Whenever we approach the health content in our science lessons we need to try to *think like scientists,* asking questions and seeking answers rather than just believing everything we have been told.

Here are some activities which link health and science, based on five themes taken from Chapter 2. All these activities can be taught using methods which teach children to 'think like scientists'. In this table and those for the other subjects, (L) means 'suitable for lower primary classes'; (M) means 'suitable for middle primary'; and (U) means 'suitable for upper primary or lower secondary'.

Thinking like scientists

TWENTY ACTIVITIES LINKING SCIENCE WITH HEALTH

Hygiene
1. Investigating hand-washing. How do we get our hands really clean? (L)
2. Investigating different ways of cleaning teeth. How can we make materials for cleaning teeth? (L)
3. How can we improve water quality? (M/U)
4. How can we make pure drinking water by evaporation and condensation? (U)
5. How can we measure air pollution? (U)
6. Experiments to show how sweet drinks rot teeth. (M)
7. Investigating the best ways of washing and drying clothes. (M/U)

Safety at home and on the roads
1. Looking at ways of putting out fires (burning needs air). (M/U)
2. Investigating what makes loads on lorries or bikes tip over (centres of gravity). (M/U)
3. Looking at how braking works, and what conditions make braking on cars and bikes more difficult (friction). (U)

continued →

Foods, vitamins and other important elements
1. Finding out what values different foods have. How different kinds of food can help us grow well and stay healthy. (L/M/U)
2. Looking at micronutrients such as iron and iodine and how these need to be present in our foods to help us stay healthy. (U)

Diseases and living things which spread them
1. Finding out how dangerous insects breed and how to prevent them breeding. (L/M)
2. Investigating how microbes make food go bad.(U)
3. Why boiling water kills bacteria. (U)
4. How germs can be passed through hands and water.
5. How epidemics such as Cholera can be spread. (M/U)

Looking at our bodies
1. Experiments about breathing.
   □ How children breathe at different rates at different ages. (M)
   □ Recognizing danger signs in breathing (when little children have infections such as pneumonia). (M)
2. Investigation (model) of how smoking makes our lungs dirty. (U)
3. Models to show how babies are born and why trained help is sometimes very important. (U)

An example of a science activity for middle primary level.

Note how this activity develops the skills of 'thinking like a scientist'.

How to keep cool using evaporation (an experiment on the best way to cool bottled water)
- Setting up the experiment. You will need:
  - six identical bottles full of water
  - four rags
  - string
  - fibre or elastic bands to hold them in place
  - a bowl of water
  - a thermometer is useful but not necessary
- Doing the experiment

Stand three bottles of water in a half-filled bowl of water in a sunny place outside the classroom. Wet one rag thoroughly and wrap it around one of the bottles letting the rag dip into the water. Wrap the second bottle with a dry rag. Stand it in the water without letting the rag get wet. Stand the third bottle in the water without a rag round it.

Put the other three bottles on the ground alongside the bowl. Cover one with a damp cloth and one with a dry cloth. Leave the third without any covering. Leave all six bottles in the sun for half an hour or longer.

- While they are waiting the children can:
▨ Draw the experiment.
▨ Predict what they think will happen and why.
▨ Put some water on their own arms and legs and tell each other how it felt when they were drying in the sun.
- Recording and discussing what happened
Record the temperature of water in the six bottles and list them in order. Which was the coolest, which was second coolest . . . which was the warmest?

Discuss what caused the bottles covered by the damp cloth to be coolest.
- Applying the knowledge to health
Discuss:
▨ How can we use the knowledge that evaporation causes cooling:
   – to lower the temperature of someone with fever (by sponging with a damp cloth);
   – to cool food or drink (put a wet cloth around the sealed food or bottle and stand in a container in water)?
▨ How else can we use the cooling power of evaporation (e.g. by sprinkling water on the ground in a court-yard, or outside a house or classroom)?
Apply to our lives:
▨ Use cool (but not cold) cloths to help people with fever feel more comfortable.
▨ Make a simple food or watercooler which works by evaporation.

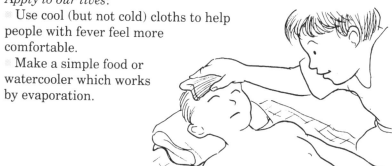

Health and mathematics

In mathematics, schools try to do two main things. First children have to learn how to use the processes of mathematics, such as working with numbers, measurement and shapes, as well as skills of estimating and recording results (often in tables and graphs). Second they have to use and apply maths to solve the problems of everyday life. Using health content is effective in both. Here are a few examples:

Maths skills

● Numbers
- Counting numbers of vehicles on a main road; averaging the number that pass in an hour (road safety campaign).
● Weighing and measuring
- Weighing babies (lessons on child growth).
- Measuring number of breaths per minute taken by a sick baby (lesson on pneumonia).
● Estimating and recording
- Estimating distance to water sources and time spent collecting water (compare with measurements later).
- Recording number of cases of malaria among children's families; making a graph of these and relating it to the amount of rainfall.
● Maths applied to healthy living
- Measuring out rehydration solution for diarrhoea
- Weighing, measuring and recording a baby's weight regularly.
- Budgeting for healthy meals, through calculating 'best buy' produce in the market.

Note: The book *Health into Mathematics* (see book list on page 166) gives many ideas. The table below gives some of the activities it suggests for five of the themes listed in Chapter 2 together with an additional vital topic, population growth.

TWENTY ACTIVITIES LINKING HEALTH AND MATHEMATICS

Body and growth monitoring
1. measuring height of younger children (M)
2. measuring around parts of the body (M)
3. measuring arm circumference (M)
4. making an age/height graph (U)
5. interpreting age-weight charts (U)

Water and sanitation
1. capacity and weight of water containers (M)
2. measuring distances from water supply (U)
3. statistics on how we use water (M)
4. costing a water supply (U)

Nutrition and breastfeeding
1. understanding ratios in mixing food (M)
2. understanding a chart comparing cases of diarrhoea among bottle-fed and breastfed babies (U)

Infectious diseases and immunization
1. class survey and survey of younger children (M/U)
2. comparing our data with national data; reading and interpreting statistics on immunization (U)
3. an illness survey (L/M)
4. the mathematics of the spread of aids (U)

Population (including timing births)
1. counting family members; comparing ages (L)
2. demonstrating population doubling and land use by using dots and folding paper (M)
3. understanding national data on population (U)
4. making predictions based on doubling times (U)
5. using percentage growth rate (U)

Example of a mathematics activity for upper primary level

Notice how this activity develops skills of accurate measurement and links this skill with real life problems.

Measuring upper arm circumference (Upper Primary)
The distance around the upper arm is used to check if younger children are suffering from undernourishment. From the first to the fifth year of life the distance around the upper arm, the arm circumference, does not change greatly. If in this time the upper arm circumference is less than 13 cm., then the child is thin. If it is less than 12 cm., the child is undernourished.

Measuring each other.

• Let the children first estimate their own upper arm circumference and those of their class mates. They can use their grip to help them make a good guess. Then they should measure using a paper strip.

The arm being measured should hang loosely at the child's side. When measuring, the strip should be halfway between the elbow and the shoulder of the left arm (see picture). The children should measure the distance to the nearest centimetre.

continued →

> • The children can measure the upper arm circumference of the youngest children in the school, or those in a nearby pre-school.
>
> They should measure to the nearest centimetre and keep a record of their results. After they have learned to measure in this way they can discuss how health workers use this measurement and whether they, as children, could use it without making other families unhappy if they found that some children were not well nourished.

Health and social studies

Social studies or environmental studies (in some cases still taught as history, geography and civics) look at the way that people live together and live in their environment. It is thus a key subject when we look at environmental health. Like science, there may be some topics which are directly health-related. But there will be other ideas and skills where health content may well be the best way of developing children's thinking and understanding.

Ideas

(Only a few health examples have been given for each of the main ideas included in the social studies programmes.)

- Living together / depending on each other
  - E.g. related to the food we eat; child growth and development; community hygiene and prevention of conditions such as worms; immunization and the prevention of epidemics.
- Living in and preserving our environment
  - E.g. effects of pollution on community health; soil conservation; food production; water management and its relation to healthy lives.
- Rights and duties of citizens
  - E.g. rights and duties in regard to health. Health issues relating to rights of women and children. A citizen's obligation to pass on effective health knowledge to others by example as well as words. Children are citizens too.
- Responsibility towards those who are 'different'
  - E.g. recognition of the relation between poverty and ill health, attitudes towards disability; towards society members (especially children) in especially difficult circumstances; for example, victims of wars and disasters; AIDS orphans.

Skills

Many learning and life skills are particularly relevant to social and environmental studies; many of these are directly relevant to health. They include:

Making and using maps

- making a plan to lay out a vegetable garden
- making a 'health map' of the neighbourhood
- locating district health services on a local map

Finding out information though community surveys
• surveying practice of local people on treating people with fever
• surveying attitudes of local people to patients with AIDS

Listening to people and understanding their views and lifestyles
• sharing information and customs regarding food and food practices
• role playing so as to understand what it feels like to be disabled
• health action activities (e.g. home safety campaign) undertaken with
children from other walks of life (say children who have not been to school).

Here are some activities possible in social studies based on five of the
main headings we identified in Chapter 2. All of them are designed to
make us think about people and places as well as learning about health.

TWENTY ACTIVITIES LINKING SOCIAL STUDIES AND HEALTH

Food

1. Eating surveys; eating diaries: What do I eat and when? What do
our little brothers and sisters eat and when? Do we eat wisely? Do
little children eat often enough? How do our customs affect our
eating habits? (L/M)

2. Food that other people eat in our communities: Getting to know
food customs of other members of the community. In what way are
they different to ours? How do they maintain a healthy diet (even
though they are eating different food to us)? (L/M)

3. Look at reasons why children in our neighbourhood, or in other
parts of our country, do not have enough food. How can we recognize
malnutrition? What can we do about it? (M/U)

4. Surveying and mapping the use of land and the conservation of the
soil: What can be done? (M/U)

5. Mapping and discussing distribution of food across the world: Who
exports and imports what? Why do some countries destroy food and
others have famine?

Safety and safe lifestyles

1. Who is responsible for safety in our home and neighbourhood?
Discussions to show that everyone has rights and responsibilities to
keep others safe. (L/M)

2. Safety past and present; how dangers and causes of accidents have
changed. Children talk to grand-parents and compare their lives with
children's own. (M)

3. Children do a road traffic survey, and map danger-places for road
accidents. (M)

4. Children learn about disasters in world safety, such as at Bhopal
(India) and Chernobyl (Ukraine); discuss causes and consequences
and who was responsible. (U)

continued →

5. Children discuss whom they admire, and how the lifestyles of these people affect older children's health and the way they act to others. (U)

Hygiene

1. Making a health map (or model) of the neighbourhood. (M)

2. Discussing pollution in the neighbourhood, focusing on things we cannot see. (M/U)

    ☐ E.g. the water looks very clean but . . . (polluted by sewage).

    ☐ The street looks tidy but . . . (mosquito larvae not killed).

    ☐ The crops are growing well but . . . (poisonous chemicals used to kill insects).

3. Map and discuss how some countries can pollute others. Involves looking at winds and ocean currents and making conclusions. (U)

Disease

1. Our responsibilities towards preventing disease. How illness of one person affects the whole family. (L/M)

2. How epidemics spread and what we can do to stop them. (U)

Child growth and development

1. Growing up. What I did; what I needed; who helped me; how I helped others at different ages. (L/M)

2. Children growing up, then and now. How families have changed but still need the same things (love, play, security). (L/M/U)

3. Children in especially difficult circumstances, such as street children, refugees, victims of war. What can other children do? (M/U)

4. Education of girls. How this affects the health of young children. (U)

5. The Declaration of Children's Rights. Who made it; what it contains; how it affects us. (U)

Example of a social studies activity for middle or upper primary level, based on the theme of safety

The following activity looks at the way that health and safety problems are usually the result of a number of causes (just like events in history). It also helps children think carefully about the consequence of actions, an important life skill.

THE 'IF ONLY' GAME

Here are four common accidents:

(1) baby drinks paraffin from a bottle;

(2) my young brother is riding my bicycle and is knocked off it by a car near the market;

(3) my little sister grabs a pot in the kitchen and burns herself;

(4) I climbed a tree near the school. The branch was rotten. I fell off and broke my arm.

Think of as many 'if only' sentences for each one. Here is the first example:
- 'If only we had put the bottle out of baby's reach.'
- 'If only we had screwed the top on tightly.'
- 'If only we did not use that kind of bottle to keep paraffin in.'
- 'If only someone had watched the baby.'
- 'If only . . .' (can you think of more?)

Now do the same for examples (2), (3) and (4)

Finally think of more possible accidents, including ones that have happened in your own families, and talk about 'if only' with these. Then discuss how it would be possible for you and your families to think more about preventing accidents.

Health and language

Most of us would think of language as being the most important of school subjects. We need to use language to communicate about things that matter. Health matters to us all. When we teach language we need to develop three different kinds of skills:
- Using the language correctly, through grammar and correct usage.
- Listening, speaking, reading and writing effectively.
- Using language as a tool for thinking and doing: finding, interpreting and working with information and ideas.

Grammar and correct usage

Children need to learn to speak and write language correctly and this involves practising grammar and sentence patterns, using past and future tenses, and learning to make simple and complicated sentences. Very often health examples can be used in this kind of practice. For example:
- Using past tenses: We immuniz*ed* the baby yesterday. We *have immunized* all our children. After we *had immunized* the baby we felt happy.
- Using conditionals: *If we immunize* the children *they will not* die of measles. *If we had immunized* that baby *he would not have* died.

Skills in effective speaking, listening, reading and writing

In Chapter 3 we presented many speaking and listening ideas under the headings *Discussion groups* and *Stories*. Here we present some additional ideas on reading and writing.

At first **reading** can be done from simple passages, just a few lines illustrating a health picture. *I play with my brother. I talk to him. He says the words I say. That is how babies learn to talk.*

My brother and I.

Writing can consist of a few sentences describing a picture, or to finish a short paragraph. *I am very careful when my little sister is crawling about in the kitchen. I* . . . .
. . . . *and* . . . .
. . . .
Later, reading and writing skills can be linked to health-related stories. Children can either start from stories which they can read or which are read to them, such as those contained in the *Child-to-Child Readers*. From these they can practise many things.

Take for instance this simple story, taken from the *Child-to-Child Reader*, 'Not Just a Cold'. Information about coughs, colds and pneumonia is found in *Children for Health* pages 124-33.

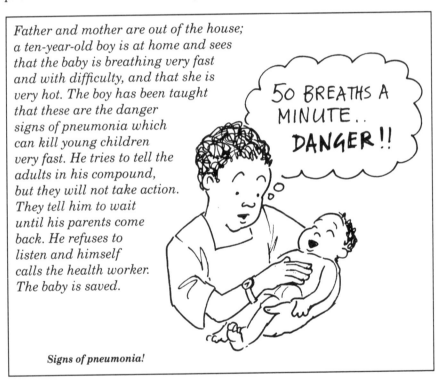

Father and mother are out of the house; a ten-year-old boy is at home and sees that the baby is breathing very fast and with difficulty, and that she is very hot. The boy has been taught that these are the danger signs of pneumonia which can kill young children very fast. He tries to tell the adults in his compound, but they will not take action. They tell him to wait until his parents come back. He refuses to listen and himself calls the health worker. The baby is saved.

Signs of pneumonia!

Based on this one story children can:

● Answer questions to make sure they have understood it. You can even set them the questions before they start reading the story, to help point them to the parts which are most important.
● Discuss it: e.g. 'Was the boy right to disobey his elders?'
● Expand it or rewrite it from other points of view (e.g. from the point of view of the health worker).
● Write other stories like it.

On the other hand children can start from a health message (*e.g. children who are angry and who behave badly often do so because they are very unhappy; we must try to find out why they act in the way they do, and then we can begin to help*). This can lead on to a story made up by the children themselves. This needs to be prepared for either by a **discussion**, or with sets of **pictures**. The four pictures shown here were prepared for a health education programme for children in refugee camps. They can either be shown to the children in the right order (1-4) or mixed up, so that children can first discuss them and put them in the correct sequence before writing about them. Children can do this exercise in twos or threes.

Another way to begin children writing is to start a story and let the children finish it. In every case the story is a good means of developing children's language because it relates to situations which relate to a real part of their own lives. (See Chapter 3 for further suggestions on follow-up from stories, including drama and role playing.)

Skills in finding and interpreting information

Finally, and especially in upper classes, health topics are a very good means of developing **study skills** in language. Here are some essential skills every child needs to know in order to learn independently and effectively as an adult. Next to each skill we have listed just one health-based example.

1. *Finding information from books*: children use a first-aid manual to find out how to treat burns.

2. *Condensing information* without losing the main points: children condense a health education pamphlet about malaria to a quarter of its original size.

3. *Taking effective notes*: children take notes from a talk on water hygiene given by the health worker.

4. *Reporting action taken*; children make a report of action they took to identify and help disabled children in the community.

5. *Group discussion and reporting*: children plan and conduct an effective discussion on how to help AIDS victims in the community.

6. *Making clear plans for action*: children plan a road safety campaign.

Health across the curriculum ... linking subjects together around a health theme

When health ideas are presented and reinforced, many subjects combine together. This usually happens in two ways. Either a school or a class agrees to emphasize a health theme over a term or a year, using all opportunities to get the ideas across, or a health topic is taught over a shorter period (perhaps over two weeks). It is usually presented in one subject, often science, and reinforced through teaching in other subjects, using whatever syllabus topics are being covered at the time. In each case it is very useful to find out what children have learned at the end of the period.

Here is an example of a larger theme (on clean, safe water) developed over a term in class 4.

Cleaner, safer water for class 4 (ten-year-olds)

In science:
• five lessons from the syllabus looking at the difference between safe and unsafe water, what diseases are spread through dirty water and how water can be made safe.

In language:
• lessons from the syllabus on how to describe things (adjectives); use examples about water, e.g. 'This clear water is not clean'; 'This boiled water is safe for babies to drink', etc.

- when children practise comprehension, one of the passages they are given is a passage about clean and dirty water.
- when children are asked to write stories, one exercise is based on reading stories about dirty water and then writing their own story and making it into a play (in groups).

In mathematics (where the syllabus covers weighing and measuring)
- children learn about the measuring capacity of water.
- they relate this to making oral rehydration drinks.
- they learn how to use common items, e.g. soft-drink tins, to measure capacity.
- they measure distances to water sources and make a simple bar graph

In social studies (where the syllabus covers 'my district')
- children map sources of water.
- they look at water supply and conservation.

In art and craft
- children design posters to protect water sources and make ladles for water pots.

In music
- older children make a 'clean water' song, and dance and perform it to the younger children.

Here is a further example of a shorter topic, 'Cholera', planned over two weeks for class 7, the top class in the school, following a report of cholera in the district. Note how the activities are more advanced and challenging than those in the last example.

Special topic . . . Preventing cholera

First
Two special health lessons, given jointly by the class teacher and the health worker. The lessons look at the causes, symptoms and treatment of cholera and emphasize that although patients suspected of cholera need to be taken immediately to the hospital, oral rehydration must be given straight away. The importance of food and water hygiene, and handwashing with soap to avoid contamination, are stressed continually.

Then
Language
Reading, listening and comprehension work based on a story of how children can help in a cholera epidemic. The *Child-to-Child* story book, *The Cholera Crisis*, can be used as a resource. Children write their own stories starting with the sentence. 'They told us in school that there had been cases of cholera in our town, but the people living round our house did not believe it ...'

continued →

Science
Children do an experiment to show how an infected latrine can pollute a well. The experiment is described in *Children for Health*, page 93. They also examine how washing fruit and vegetables with infected water can spread diseases such as cholera.

Maths
Children do a survey of how water at home is made safe, what water is used for washing dishes and vegetables, and how utensils are dried. They then show the result on graphs and work out ratios, e.g. how many households dried dishes in the sun and how many did not.

Social studies
Children make a map of water sources and a flow chart of water collection and use. They discuss at which points the water could become contaminated.

Art and music
Children make posters and songs to perform on the 'Keep Away Cholera' march which the school has organized in the community.

QUESTIONS FOR EVERYONE

Planning programmes

How can we plan our programmes so that they introduce health ideas and reinforce them across the curriculum. . .

- ...when we plan programmes and write books at central level?
- ...when we make plans at school level?
- ...when we make schemes of work at classroom level (particularly if one teacher teaches all or most of the subjects)?

Materials

Can textbooks, teachers' guides, or teacher' notes be produced, which help teachers link subjects across the curriculum?

- Can we use or modify some of those which already exist such as *Health into Mathematics* or the *Child-to-Child Readers*?
- Can we 'write in' examples into new textbooks (e.g. comprehension passages about health issues in new language and reading schemes)?
- Can we write and distribute suggestions for linked activities at local level, for students in colleges or for those who attend in-service training?

Training

Can 'Health across the curriculum' be incorporated in teacher training courses...

- ...during initial training?
- ...during in-service training, including training which is school based?
In both cases most ideas should be suggested *by* teachers rather than *to* them.

Assessment

Can tests, assignments and examinations which are designed to test skills (e.g. problem-solving in mathematics, experimental techniques in science, or comprehension in language) contain health-related content?

IDEAS FOR

 ## POLICY MAKERS

- Every school to needs to develop health activities *in* and *out* of the school.
- School health committees can involve children, teachers and parents together in making schools healthier.
- Organizations and activities which encourage children to be partners in health promotion need support. They need to involve all children who wish to participate. Selective programmes, with children sometimes called 'little doctors', have many disadvantages.

 ## PROGRAMME DESIGNERS

- Health programmes and curriculum statements should contain suggestions for activities which take place around the school and from school to community.
- Checklists for *health-promoting schools* are valuable and could be designed.
- National health campaigns are valuable, but need careful planning in order to give initiative to schools and children, rather than merely using them as agents to pass on nationally devised information and slogans.

 ## LOCAL PLANNERS, MANAGERS AND TRAINERS

- School hygiene, water supply and sanitation are essential for good health. Latrines and handwashing facilities, together with safe drinking water, are the first priority.
- Health fairs, health camps, and 'healthy school' competitions raise awareness and are very popular but need much organization. Do not try too much too soon.

 ## SCHOOL AND COMMUNITY

- When heads are interested and committed the school follows.
- Children as partners in health promotion need to be encouraged and trusted, but also helped, supported and guided.

Health Beyond the Classroom

● Promoting better school hygiene and sanitation ● Promoting
better nutrition and food safety; what schools can do ● How teachers
and children can promote better health through example ● Ways of
encouraging children to take responsibility for the health of others
● The role of the head in school health promotion ● Working with
the community to promote better health ● Clubs, scouts and other
school/community activities involving children

---

1. Health around the school

Every school needs to be as safe and healthy as it can be, not only for the
benefit of the teachers and pupils but also to set a good example to the
community. As we saw in Chapter 1, the school comprises not only the
buildings and surroundings but also *all* the people who work in it and
with it.

The buildings and surroundings

In every school the buildings and surroundings need to be as safe, clean
and attractive as possible. This is much easier in some schools than
others. Some schools are well built and decorated, have adequate
furniture and sound roofs. Their doors and windows are weatherproof
and insect-proof. But the majority of schools in poor urban areas and in
rural areas do not have these advantages. Many heads teachers and
children have to work in unsuitable or crowded buildings and some even
lack sufficient classrooms and furniture. But even the most difficult
situation can usually be made cleaner, safer and more attractive.

● Buildings and surroundings can be swept.
● Grass can be cut down. (This also helps ensure safety from insects
and snakes.)
● Trees and flowers can be planted and looked after.
● Refuse containers can be made from wood and fibre; pits may be dug.
● Children can encourage each other to keep the surroundings clean
and tidy.
● Parents and community leaders can persuade people in the
neighbourhood to respect the school buildings and surroundings and
not to pollute them; in rural areas they can persuade them to keep
animals out of the school premises.

Water supplies and hygiene

Infection from stools through dirty hands is the most common and most easily prevented source of diarrhoea, and many other diseases. The best health resources a school can provide are adequate and clean latrines together with clean drinking water, and water for washing hands. The building of school latrines needs to be high on every school's priority list. One latrine needs to be provided for every class of forty children.

But even when latrines and water supply are poor or even lacking it is still possible to improve hygiene practices by:

- making sure that the safest possible toilet rules are made and that children keep them;
- providing enough clean safe water for drinking and handwashing;
- burning or burying rubbish which encourages flies breeding.

Food and food safety

Most schools are not fortunate enough to be able to supply food to children. If they do they should know how important it is to serve a good diet to children, to store and protect the food well and to monitor the cooks to see that they are clean and free from disease. More often children have to bring or buy food. In some schools there are special shops or stands run or monitored by the school. This is by far the best way of controlling the type and cleanliness of food sold. In other cases there are food vendors.

Here are a few actions that any school can take.

1. Encourage all children to eat a meal before coming to school. (Often children attend school without having breakfast, because they leave home very early or come to afternoon sessions in double-shift schools without having a meal – because the family mid-day meal is later. In both cases their work suffers.)

2. Monitor the meals which children bring to school, and discuss with parents how these can be made more nutritious at no extra cost.

3. Monitor the food-sellers. Make sure that their food is covered and that they themselves are clean. Children can help here. In some countries, school-food-sellers have to have a medical check-up.

4. Advise children on the best food to buy. Encourage food-sellers to sell this.

5. Stress to children the importance of clean hands when eating. (Children can help to monitor each other).

Check

- Buildings
  - ☐ clean; repaired; safe?
- Hygiene
  - ☐ clean latrines; water for handwashing and safe water for drinking; good refuse disposal?
- Compound
  - ☐ clean; attractive; free from health hazards?
- Safety for Children
  - ☐ road and other safety hazards monitored?
- Food safety
  - ☐ hygiene of food-sellers monitored?

Setting a good example: the pupils and their teachers

Everyone would agree, that a community judges a school partly by the appearance and behaviour of its pupils and teachers. For this reason all schools should insist that their pupils and staff are clean and well dressed, and that they behave well to outsiders.

But in a health-promoting school we are also looking for other signs of health behaviour. We are looking for teachers who take a real interest in their own health and in helping others to stay healthy, who are prepared to give something extra (usually their free time) to help promote health in the school community.

Something extra: helping parents.

Later on in this chapter we describe how teachers need to be involved both in setting up and running school health committees and in organizing school health clubs.

We are looking for pupils, girls and boys, who are interested not only in their own health but in the health of their families and friends and particularly in that of the younger children who look up to them. One way of encouraging children to help each other is by pairing older children from higher classes with younger ones from the first class or from pre-primary classes attached to the school.

Sometimes these are called 'school sisters or school brothers' and in many schools it is the younger children who are asked to choose their older 'brother' or 'sister'. It is very important that older children realize that this relationship goes much beyond just seeing that the smaller children are clean and tidy. An 'older sister' or 'older brother' needs to develop into a good example, a good friend, a teacher and a protector all at the same time.

HOW CHILDREN CAN HELP THEIR 'BROTHERS' OR 'SISTERS'

- Make toys or books for reading. Make games and play with them.
- Teach them simple health songs and singing games.
- Show them simple health skills, e.g. washing hands, cleaning a cut.
- Keep them safe and show them how to keep safe.
  (This includes making sure that older children do not bully them.)
- Help them bring and buy good food.
- Plant vegetables and trees with them.

Check

- **Children**
  - Clean?
  - Active in making their school healthier?
- Helpful to others (especially younger children and old people)?
  - Interested in and concerned about improving health?
  - Proud of their school?

Check

- **Teachers**
  - Clean and neat?
  - Show example of healthy lifestyles?
  - Knowledgeable about health; concerned about the health of the school children and their families?
  - Proud of their school's health and hygiene?
- Active in linking with the community?

Children taking responsibility

| *Pairing* | *Health monitors* | *Children's health committee* |

Later in this chapter we will be talking about school health committees, which can include teachers, community members and children's representatives. These should review the health of the school. In addition it is useful to involve children in the day-to-day management of school health. Many ways have been tried successfully. They include:

- electing 'health monitors' for each class or, better still, letting children take turns to act as health monitors;
- helping to organize health days with parents and health campaigns from school to community;
- electing a children's health committee with one teacher as adviser to oversee a range of health matters in the school;
- choosing a school 'ministry of health', probably with assistant ministers for food, safety, hygiene and agriculture (growing vegetables), each with a suitable number of assistants;
- making voluntary groups such as health action clubs or health scouts (described later) responsible for certain aspects of school health or hygiene, reporting to the school health committee.

It is important that children choose their representatives, that they are give real responsibilities (as they are at home). *The activities must be looked on as something interesting and enjoyable rather than just an extra school duty.* This means that the children must receive support when they need it, and that they are not set dirty or heavy work such as cultivating fields, cleaning rubbish dumps or digging latrines. They are always to be praised and encouraged for the work they do.

THINGS A CHILDREN'S HEALTH COMMITTEE CAN DO

- Supervise and encourage school cleanliness.
- Help make the school an attractive place.
- Promote gardening and tree planting.
- Monitor the school brother and sister scheme.
- Oversee safety in the school and the road near it.
- Look after food cleanliness of food-sellers at school.
- See that water used in the school is clean and safe and that children use it cleanly.
- Eliminate mosquito-breeding places near the school
- Help organize a school dispensary or first-aid post.
- Maintain close links with the local health workers.
- Make up health quizzes and health check lists and try them out.

Health around the school: what can the head teacher do?

When head teachers are really interested in health promotion in their schools, the teachers and children follow their lead. There are many ways that heads can show leadership. They need, of course, to help set up and encourage all the activities mentioned earlier, but in addition there are four other issues worth considering.

- **School health rules**

Would it be profitable to agree with staff, and probably with children as well, a set of simple health rules that could be kept by all school members?

- **Standards (and monitoring)**

Could a checklist be drawn up and monitored from time to time by children and teachers to see 'how the school is doing?' (Chapter 9)

- **Assemblies**

Could assemblies be regularly used to present health messages and ideas, usually done by the children themselves in different ways such as stories, poems, song or drama?

- **Themes**

Could schools choose health themes (see Chapter 4 and Chapter 7) to be reinforced and monitored over a week, a month or a term?

2. Schools and their communities

Involvement and cooperation: school; parents; community leaders

In order for a school to set a good health example it needs to have the cooperation of the parents. Parents need to help the school just as schools need to help and involve parents

> ### Check
> - **The parents**
>   - interested in the health of children;
>   - cooperative and supportive of school health activities;
>   - receptive to new ideas from the school;
>   - proud of the health activities undertaken by their children

Child *with* family

Although we usually speak of 'child TO child' we may be better to think of 'child WITH family'. Often we think of children in school 'taking messages to their parents'. This may not be the best way of linking school with home. Instead we need to think of children *sharing* what they have learnt with their families, and of parents in turn letting schools know what children have done at home. This means that the school needs to *share* with parents the health priorities which it has identified, and to *consult* the community on what they might wish children to learn and how they might wish them to contribute to community health.

Can we show you what we have learnt at school?

As we mentioned in Chapter 2, schools should realize that some topics such as road safety or preventing malaria can be easily communicated to parents, while others such as food and disability are likely to be more culturally sensitive.

This is why developing life skills, such as effective ways of communicating with adults, is so important, and teachers must seek to develop these with children. Children *can* discuss difficult issues with their families provided they think very carefully about what to say and how and when to say it. Teachers should therefore be very careful about how they approach such issues, and they should discuss them very carefully with children with parents and with community leaders. Once a community begins to say 'our school is teaching children to contradict their elders', then confidence is lost and partnership between school and community weakens.

It is also important to remember that there are many things that children can do at home which are useful and important and yet in no way bring them into conflict with their parents and older people. They include:

- playing and making safe toys for younger children, reading to them and showing them pictures;
- keeping younger children safe and clean;
- growing plants and vegetables;
- making useful things for the house such as food and water covers, ladles, water filters, rat traps and many other items;
- practising good hygiene;.
- preventing insects (e.g. mosquitoes) from breeding. . . and many more.

A school health committee

One way of linking schools with their communities is to establish a school health committee. This needs to be quite small but composed of people who will attend regularly. It could meet three time a year and could be convened for special meetings when there was a need (such as an epidemic or a particular problem with hygiene, water supply or safety identified by the school). Membership can vary according to the health needs and the nature of the community. Possible membership might be: the Head; one teacher (the school health coordinator); the local health worker responsible for the school; a representative of the school food vendors; two or three parents or other interested community members (probably chosen by the Parent Teachers' Association); and two children.

THINGS A SCHOOL HEALTH COMMITTEE CAN DO

● Help to set priority health themes for the school.

● Decide on how to approach government and community leaders, to make the school a healthier and safer place (e.g. by building latrines, calming traffic on the roads, and removing rubbish and other pollution).

● Help to promote links between school and local health programmes, health centres and health services.

● Take steps to improve the safety and security of the school, e.g. fencing, watchmen.

● Design and follow up monitoring activities (e.g. a healthy school checklist).

● Receive reports from the children's health committee and encourage them in the work they are doing.

● Agree times and topics of any fair, campaign or open day which the school may hold (see next section).

● React quickly to specific health needs and emergencies.

When parents come to school

Many schools organize 'open days', usually once a year. If schools or classes have agreed special health themes for the year or the term, children can be asked to describe what they have done to improve health in the school and to pass on the priority health ideas they have learnt through posters they have made, or through songs, poems, plays and puppet shows they have created.

In some countries schools also organize special health fairs in which the children and the whole community enjoy an afternoon at the school where they learn and practise good health at the same time. Health fairs are also sometimes organized by groups of neighbouring schools. If head teachers cooperate with local health workers, such health fairs can be very successful and enjoyable. The school health committee can help to plan the fair and the children's health committee could organize it.

ACTIVITIES POSSIBLE AT A HEALTH FAIR

- Dances, drama, songs and puppet shows by children.
- Games and stalls with health messages.
- Judging a health poster, or a song or story competition.
- A quiz competition for children and adults.
- Talks and demonstrations by local health workers.
- Food stalls selling vegetables grown by the children and healthy snacks made by them.
- Free first-aid teaching.
- Toys and games made by children for sale.

Campaigns and action projects in the community

Sometimes schools wish to become involved in national health campaigns, for instance on road safety, AIDS awareness or immunization. Sometimes there may be local campaigns relating to particular epidemics or health problems. Sometimes smaller scale action projects can be initiated by the school or the local community. In every case it is important for schools to work hand in hand with others such as health or agricultural workers.

POSSIBLE CAMPAIGNS

- Learn about AIDS
- Immunization
- Road Safety
- Soil conservation
- Nutrition
- Helping the disabled

POSSIBLE ACTION PROJECTS

- Toy-making for children in créches
- Growing vegetables and fruit trees
- Aids for disabled children
- Helping local old people
- Protecting water sources
- Tree planting

When campaigns are organized it is important that teaching and other out-of-class activities in schools prepare children for the campaign and discuss what they have done afterwards. In this way they will remember the messages much better. It is also always important to involve children in activities which develop their imagination and make them think. Those who organize national campaigns often use children as 'loudspeakers', singing a prepared song; shouting prepared slogans; or performing a prepared play. Let them continue these but also let them add to them by encouraging children to performing their own drama, write their own poems or stories, draw their own pictures, invent and make their own banners.

Remember: Activities such as health campaigns or action projects are excellent ways of linking schools with communities and of raising the image of the school, but they take time. Never try to organize more than one of these in any one term.

3. Health clubs and health scouts

Sometimes schools organize special health clubs in addition to the learning which takes place in class. Sometimes, where there is little emphasis placed on health in the school programme, the health club is the main way in which children learn to take health action.

Different kinds of clubs and groups

Many schools already have health clubs (Health Action clubs; Child-to-Child clubs; Child Survival clubs; Red Cross clubs). Scouts and Guides also take an interest in health. In some countries there are Health Scouts or Little Doctor programmes which are based on the school but which work largely in the community. It is usually wise to have only one health-related group in a school, otherwise rivalries develop and it becomes difficult for staff to give the time necessary to help.

In some countries schools organize summer clubs when children come to school for a certain time during the holidays and spend their time doing 'fun' activities related to health. In other places still, children from a number of schools combine to take part in 'health camps' for a few days. Both these can be very popular, but before starting them, organizers will need to find out how many children will wish to attend and for how long, who will be able to organize them and how these organizers can be supported. It is always best to start with a small and manageable programme. It can be expanded later. If a large out-of-school programme is launched and fails, it is often difficult to revive it.

Who attends health clubs and scout groups?

Some 'Little Doctor' programmes make it difficult for children to join. Numbers are restricted. Children are chosen because they are good at school work, because they are well dressed and healthy or because they have passed some kind of entrance test. This policy needs to be questioned since:

• it may send the wrong message to the children and their parents. 'Some people are experts on health. . . Others need only passively to follow their advice.' In this book we have stressed that *all citizens have responsibilities about their own health and for passing on knowledge to others*;

• it may mean that children from more privileged families become the health scouts or 'little doctors'. Those who are not chosen are, yet again, those who have less support at home and who need the experience most.

It is, therefore, better to let all those who are keen take part in these programmes which improve not only their knowledge and skills but also develop their self-respect and self-confidence. If organizers have doubts they should organize children in twos or threes so that the 'stronger' children help the 'weaker' ones.

Organizing health clubs and scout groups

Although children themselves should be involved in helping to plan and organize their meetings they will need a lot of help and support. If they go into the community they must be very closely supervised. Everyone should understand what they are doing and why. They should probably not be called 'doctors' or 'nurses' and certainly never allowed to behave as if they have special knowledge which others cannot have. As 'health scouts' or 'junior health workers' they will still be greatly welcomed because they are finding out useful information and sharing useful knowledge with others.

It is vital that the club identify an active and knowledgeable health adviser who can provide accurate and up-to-date health information and make sure that children are passing it on correctly. **Remember: knowledge and practice change. Last year's treatment may not beat this year's germs**.

It is often profitable to organize meetings around the four-step approach described in Chapter 3 of this book. In this way children will have time to understand a problem well, and to turn that understanding into action. On the next page is an example of the work of a health scout meeting, taken from the *Child-to-Child Resource Book* but based on real experience.

HEALTH SCOUT GROUPS ... FIVE MEETINGS ON IMMUNIZATION

First meeting (recognize and understand)
- Group leader talks about immunization.
- Health worker attends, tells stories from her experience.
- Children play a game called 'Antibodies and Germs'.

Between meetings scouts do a survey of children in the neighbourhood. Each scout takes five families. Who has been immunized? Did they complete the whole series?

Second meeting (plan)
- Discuss the results of the survey.
- Make up an immunization song.
- Make record cards to remind families when immunization is due.
- Make posters with immunization times on them.

Between meetings pass on the record cards and tell the families about the times of the clinics. Put up the posters (with permission).

Third meeting (plan and act)
- Plan and rehearse an immunization play (including songs).
- Decide when it will be shown.
- Plan the discussion following the performance.

Between the meetings, perform the play at the community centre. The health worker attends to help with the discussion.

Fourth meeting (act)
- At the time of the clinic, scouts help to bring along the young children.
- They help to complete the record cards.
- They amuse children while waiting.

Between the meetings, scouts prepare reports of what they did at the clinic ready for the next meeting.

Fifth meeting (evaluate)
- The health worker and the scouts discuss what they have done and how they could continue it.
- They decide they will create a special 'immunization badge' and work out activities.

Some 'DOs' and 'DON'Ts' for club organizers

DO

• Involve children in planning and organization.

• Encourage a programme with plenty of activity.

• Organize activities in a sequence so that children have plenty of time to understand about the health problem they are looking at and can then move on to action.

• Make sure that the activities are fun to do.

• Use the club members to mobilize other children they know to become involved in health activities.

• Make sure that children are given some form of recognition (badges or certificates).

• Remember that all health information given to and by children must be accurate and up-to-date.

DON'T

• Underestimate them and do all the organization for them.

• Organize too many talks without practical follow up.

• Organize too many activities which are not connected with each other, and which children never really follow up well.

• Make children do activities they do not want to do (or which no-one else wants to do).

• Let club members believe that these activities are 'just for them'.

• Take what the children are doing for granted and forget to praise and encourage them.

• Forget to involve the health workers.

QUESTIONS FOR EVERYONE

Health around the school (buildings and surroundings)

- What realistic steps can schools take to improve the school environment and make it more healthy?

- How can we emphasize the priority of adequate water supply and sanitation for schools, and persuade communities and local authorities to take action.

Health around the school (The head, the teachers, the children)

- How can we motivate heads to show leadership in health promotion?

- Could all schools be encouraged to form health committees, or should the practice be allowed to grow naturally?

- Would inter-school competitions (based on a 'healthy school checklist') be valuable and popular?

- How can we recognize and encourage schools where children take a real interest in making their own school healthier?

Schools and their communities

- How can we ensure that children do take health messages to their families and communities without raising criticism from adults?

- How can we plan a programme of events such as open days, campaigns or fairs, which it is realistic to operate and acceptable given other pressures on schools?

- How can we best involve parents in health-promotion activities?

- How can we ensure the best cooperation between health and education at local level?

Clubs and Scout groups

- How and when can we promote and organize such groups?

- How can we make sure that all children who wish to take part have the benefit of working in these groups?

IDEAS FOR

POLICY MAKERS AND PROGRAMMERS

- School health services require cooperation at every level between education and health sectors.
- The first aim of health services is to prevent ill health and suffering from occurring. The second is to find out problems as early as possible and take action to meet them. The third is to deal with problems which are long term but need to be managed so that they will not get worse.
- Health workers alone cannot meet these aims. They must be met in partnership with the school and the community.
- In addition to disease prevention, health policies in school need to reflect safety and environmental health as well as mental and emotional health.

LOCAL PLANNERS, MANAGERS AND TRAINERS

- Health Workers need to plan their activities carefully. Their skills are important, their time is limited. They can pass on their knowledge and skills to the teachers, the parents, and the children in schools, who can then help them in providing services.
- Activities such as weighing and measuring all schoolchildren may not prove the best use of the limited time available to health workers.
- Activities such as organizing campaigns to de-worm children and to ensure they are provided with essential micronutrients such as Vitamin A, Iodine and Iron can make a great impact on health.

SCHOOL AND COMMUNITY

- The local health worker is a key resource person for schools and for the families of school children.
- All people in school, including children themselves, have an important part to play in providing health services. Health problems can occur at any time.
- The role of children is particularly important as they may be the first to notice that others are in difficulties and they are often the best people available to help comfort and reassure their fellow pupils.

CHAPTER 6

Health Services For and From the School

> ● Health services, as a partnership involving health workers, school and community members, are based on the prevention of ill health at three levels.
>
> **1.** Stopping ill health from occurring (environment, nutrition, immunization, safety, promoting life skills).
>
> **2.** Identifying problems and taking action early (health checks and resulting action, identifying and helping children with mental and emotional problems, quick action in case of illness, first aid).
>
> **3.** Managing health problems 'which will not go away'.

In the past many of us have thought that health services should be provided for the school by people from outside it, usually doctors, nurses and other health workers. Our new concept of comprehensive health care is rather different. The health professionals play a very important role but they work in partnership with the head, the teachers and the children on the one hand, and with the parents and the community on the other. Together these provide health care which is *for* the school, *in* the school and *from* school to the community and which can be delivered both when the health workers are there and when they are not.

Health workers

Heads, teachers and children

Community members

Working together to provide health services

Three levels of health services in and for school

Health services for schools seek to help children in three ways:
- by preventing disease and ill health from affecting their lives;
- by taking action to help children immediately where this is possible;
- by referring them to expert help where necessary.

Remember: health problems are not just physical, they can be mental and emotional as well (see Chapter 1).

There are three stages at which action can be taken.

Stage 1: Stopping ill health from happening: this is the first level of prevention and action.

Stage 2: Identifying problems early and taking action straight away, to stop things getting worse: this is the second level of prevention and action.

Stage 3: Managing ill health and suffering which children have to 'live with' (such the effects of illness, disabilities, and emotional problems), so that there is always someone there to help and to make sure that action is taken if it is needed and the problem is not allowed to get worse. This is the third level.

Let us take these stages one by one and see how our three partners can provide health services at each stage.

Stage 1
The first level of prevention and action

There are six key actions here:

1. Actions to promote good practices in water and sanitation

These have been stressed in Chapter 5. *Nothing is more important for school health than good hygiene practices, enough latrines, and clean water for handwashing and safe water for drinking.*

How health and environmental sanitation workers can help
- by educating teachers and communities on WHY sanitation, particularly proper management of stools, is important to the health of children;
- by advising schools on how many latrines they need and of what kind, also what action they should take if they cannot afford to build latrines;
- by advising schools on how to keep their water supplies clean and how to use them wisely;
- by putting pressure on authorities to spend money on school hygiene.

How teachers, pupils and the community can help
- by ensuring that hygiene is properly taught and that hygiene and water practices are observed *all day and every day* at school and at home;

- by ensuring that the younger children (the next generation of school children) are well grounded in good hygiene habits;
- by helping to raise money and provide labour to make school hygiene better;
- by using their influence to persuade authorities to improve school hygiene.

2. Actions to improve the nutrition of school children and of the community

In previous chapters we have stressed the need to ensure that children and their families eat the best food available for them, that they eat frequently enough and at the most effective times (e.g. that children do not miss meals as a result of attending school), and that girls are given as much food as boys. We have stressed that families need to be encouraged to send children to school with the most nutritious food and that food-sellers should be encouraged to sell it and keep it clean. It is also very important that children and their families receive enough of certain key vitamins and minerals in their diets.(We sometimes call these *micronutrients*.) Three are particularly important, namely **vitamin A**, **iodine** and **iron** (see Appendix page 173 for further information).

How can the three partners help to provide primary prevention through better nutrition?

How health workers can help
- by making sure that teachers spread correct and up-to-date nutrition messages including those about micronutrients;
- by emphasizing the importance of nutrition within the community, using the radio where possible to reinforce their messages, especially 'new' ones such as the importance of using iodized salt or oil;
- by trying to make sure that government advice regarding food supplements is made known and followed. Whenever possible it is important to counter *false rumours*, which seem always to spread, about the effects of any new medical policy affecting food or medicine: e.g. 'The new oil or salt will make us weak', or 'They are giving our children these new pills to stop us having more children.'

How teachers, children and their parents can help
- by teaching and learning that a well-chosen and well-balanced diet, chosen from food which is locally available and affordable, develops children's bodies *and their minds*;
- by ensuring that children eat wisely and bring the right food to school and that food-sellers cooperate in selling nutritious foods;
- by helping to make sure that the next generation of children (the babies at home) are eating well. Breastfeeding and good weaning practices are particularly important;
- by growing and eating fruit and dark-green leafy vegetables.

- by cooperating in any national or local schemes to provide the micronutrients which children may be lacking, and by persuading others to cooperate.

3. Action to make sure that children and their family are given *immunization* against certain diseases

Health workers need to check that children in school were immunized when they were babies and that they receive any immunizations recommended during the years they are at school. Even more important, health workers need to persuade the school to pass on the immunization message to families through **teachers and children**.

4. Action to make sure that children understand how their bodies change at puberty and how to protect themselves at that age against the threat of drugs (including smoking and alcohol) and of STDs and AIDS

Teachers will be mainly responsible for passing on this vital knowledge and these skills, but they need help from **health workers** on visual aids and methods. **Parents** need to support this teaching and need to be reminded of the evidence from a large numbers of studies that *sex education does NOT encourage children to be more sexually active, rather the knowledge helps them to avoid STDs and early pregnancy.*

5. Action to improve *safety* at school and to teach children how to prevent accidents at home

Teachers can monitor school safety; they can also encourage **children** to make surveys of 'accidents waiting to happen' at home and at school, to pass on information to **parents** and to be watchful of younger children in their charge.

6. Action to develop life skills and attitudes in children so that they learn to feel responsibility and to acquire confidence to take wise decisions regarding their own health

Stage 2
The second level of prevention and action

There are three main areas here:

1. Checking the physical health of children in school so as to detect health problems early

This includes:

● **Checking for signs of disease, in its early stages.**
Certain diseases such as chronic malaria, asthma, and tuberculosis (a growing threat) can be discovered early by check-ups. When children have anaemia, through lack of iron and infection by hookworm, this is also easy to detect.

● **Checking for *signs of worms and parasites* which can affect the general health of the child.**
Certain *parasites* such as ringworm, scabies and lice can easily be seen. They spread fast from one child to another. Action needs to be taken quickly to avoid all children becoming infected. Parasites can weaken whole communities. In many countries large programmes to 'de-worm' children are planned regularly (see Appendix page 171 for further information). In some countries, especially in Africa, Bilharzia, a parasite which enters the blood stream and is present in slow-moving water, is also a very serious threat.

● **Checking that children are *growing and developing* steadily.**
There is a need to identify children who are underweight, and those who show signs of malnutrition as well as children who are very small (often a sign of poor feeding at home when they are young). It is also important to identify children who do not gain weight over a period of time. All this means that regular checks are necessary.

Usually problems in growth and development start with families at home and may also affect younger children from the same family who will be attending school in the next years.

● **Checking *teeth and gums* for signs of decay or other problems.**

● **Checking for *physical problems* such as flat feet and for *signs of disability* such as difficulties in moving, hearing or seeing.**
Sometimes these are very evident. Sometimes they are much less easy to detect. Indeed many children with sight and hearing problems do not know that they have them because they have known nothing else.

Not stupid! Can't see the board properly.

Not disobedient! Can't hear well.

Although some children are born with disabilities, many others can develop them during their school years – sometimes as a result of diseases such as measles or lack of the right food and vitamins. Therefore children need to be checked regularly. Sometimes simple actions, such as changing a child's seating in class, can make all the difference for a child who has difficulties in seeing and hearing.

How health workers can help

There are some actions (such as checking for signs of illnesses such as TB, and for physical signs such as those of hernias or an enlarged spleen) which *only* health workers can do. However, numbers of health workers are limited, schools are many, and time spent on visits needs to be used as effectively as possible.

Remember: it may *not* be a wise use of a health worker's time to weigh and measure all children when they visit a school, especially if they do not have time to come back regularly to follow this up.

Instead, health workers can play a vital role in:
- Undertaking medical checks on all children who enter school (and, if resources permit, children in their last year of school).
- Advising staff and children on how and when to take action:
   through keeping records of their own height and weight;
   through checking for signs of worms and parasites and either treating them themselves or referring them to the health centre as they are advised;
   through noticing signs of disability and referring these to the health workers for further checking;
   through noting signs of serious illness.
- Monitoring *selected* pupils who have been identified as having special health problems.
- Helping pupils referred to them by their teachers or parents. Pupils may have physical problems, but also social ones.

How teachers, children and parents can help

- By keeping their own records of height, weight and illness.
In many cases this can be linked to mathematics teaching. Every class could have its own measuring scale marked on a door or wall. Special scales are now available (see Chapter 10). Weighing scales are often available in health centres and sometimes in the community, for weighing farm produce. Children could be given the responsibility of keeping regular records and reporting results to the school health education committee or coordinator. If many children in a school are failing to gain weight or are found to be short or small for their age, the head needs to inform local health workers.
- By running their own 'Wormwatch' and ' Skinwatch' programmes, to

try to rid children of parasites. This can be linked in with a national or local de-worming programme, and with lessons on hygiene and sanitation.

• By becoming aware and reporting problems with teeth and gums.

• By learning how to watch out for signs of disability or disease among their pupils and friends or among younger children for whom they have a responsibility. Children need, for instance, to look for and report if their friends:

have a bad cough, or difficulties in breathing

seem to have fever or have bad headaches or stomach aches

suffer vomiting and diarrhoea

seem not hear or see well

have skin problems

are always sad or aloof

• By keeping a close eye on children's academic work in the classroom and noticing when children are not performing as well as they should do. This may often be a sign of some physical or emotional problem (see below).

2. Looking out for children with mental *and emotional problems* and finding ways in which these can be helped

MENTAL OR EMOTIONAL PROBLEMS, SOME SIGNS TO LOOK FOR:

The child:

• Suddenly begins to lose interest in school work.

• Doesn't do homework or does it very poorly.

• Doesn't play with friends; sits alone.

• Becomes unhelpful in class.

• Looks unhappy and cries often, e.g. when work or classroom behaviour is criticized.

• Gets angry and violent with other children much more often than usual.

• Does not seem to take an interest in looking neat and clean.

• Regularly forgets to do what he or she has been asked.

• Acts in other ways which are not usual ones.

Schools are often quick to spot physical illness but slow to realize that children who are 'slow', 'sleepy', 'lazy', 'unfriendly', ' unhelpful ', ' rude' or 'naughty' may be suffering from mental and emotional problems.

Many children and adults have these problems. Most can be helped at home and in school by love, attention, understanding and kindness. Only in rare cases is there need for medical action. In order to help, teachers and other children need to be able to *listen* to the child who is unhappy so that they can understand the problem, or find someone else the child wants to talk to. More often than not they will find that there are difficulties in the home and this will require establishing close links with the family. Home problems can include violence to children, too much work at home, fights and quarrels between adults, difficulties caused by drink and drugs, problems of poverty, sickness and death in the home (including special problems when family members have AIDS) and many others.

In a good number of cases, however, the problems lie in the school itself, particularly in bullying. Some teachers have taken the view that bullying has always gone on in schools and should be overlooked. We completely disagree.

Bullying is often the sign of serious problems within a community, and often within the families of the children who practise it. Children who bully are often those who later discriminate against those who are weak in a community and those who are different. They are a threat to the social health of a community. They must be shown very early that their actions are wrong. Children who are bullied can be very badly affected. Their lives are made unhappy and their school work suffers. Some children who have been bullied have even tried to kill themselves.

How health and social workers can help

Health workers and social workers can help by giving advice to children and families who have been identified, and by finding people within the community who can help them and, in a few cases, referring those with severe problems to specialists for help.

They can help by advising and training teachers (including students in colleges and on courses) how to recognize signs of mental and emotional difficulties and how to recognize the danger signs of severe problems. They can advise them about what they can do to help. They can help children's groups such as health clubs in the same way. They can speak to parents groups.

How children, teachers and parents can help

Notice that we have put children first. They may be the first to notice problems and difficulties with their fellow pupils. Other children may tell them things they do not tell adults. Older children are often the best comforters for younger ones and the first to notice if they are being bullied in big school. Remember that if a large majority of children in a school oppose bullying, it will not happen.

Teachers and parents also have a vital role to play in listening to their children, giving them support and trying to solve their problems. One of the most important lessons for them to learn is to see the world from the child's point of view. Once they can do this it is much easier to help.

Bullies not welcome

3. Taking action when accidents happen

As stressed earlier, some safety problems are present in schools. However, even more accidents take place on the way to school and at home. A school needs to prepare children to take action at home, particularly when they are looking after younger children.

If every child in every school were taught …
- to keep little children away from cooking pots,
- to keep poisons (including medicines and paraffin) out of reach,
- to bathe burns immediately with cold water,
- to clean cuts immediately with water and soap,
- to call for help immediately when a child has had a serious burn or fall or has swallowed something,
… many deaths and much serious illness would be prevented.

In school all children should be taught road safety and 'play safety' and as many teachers and older children as possible should learn first aid. **First aid saves lives.**

A simple first-aid box should be kept and stocked. National programmes or local health workers can advise on contents.

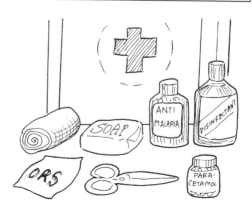

Stage 3
The third level of prevention

Often children who attend school have health problems which will not go away quickly. There are four main categories:
● long term medical problems such as asthma, or epilepsy;
● disabilities;
● poverty, which often leads to under-nourishment;
● long-term emotional problems at home such as those which affect children whose parents are very ill (perhaps with AIDS) or who have had terrible experiences such as families who have been victims of war.

How health and social workers can help

● by watching and helping these children and their families as much as possible;
● by advising teachers and parents how to deal with these children day by day;
● by suggesting how to treat particular problems which may come up from time to time, such as an attack of epilepsy or a burst of violent behaviour from a boy who himself has been a victim of violence;
● by working with other children, particularly those who are members of health clubs and health committees, advising them about how they can help their friends and classmates who need their support.

How teachers, parents and children can help

Knowledge and attitudes are vital, especially those in other children. Once children with problems can feel that they are accepted by other children and not different from them, then they can live and learn happily at school.

QUESTIONS FOR EVERYONE

Present policies

• Are our present health services in schools as effective as they could be (given the resources that there are)? Could priorities be revised? Could time be better used?

• How well are partnerships between education and health sectors working in our system? Could they be made closer?

Levels of health prevention

• Do heads, teachers, children and parents realize how much they can do in *primary*, *secondary* and *tertiary* prevention? Would they be willing to do more (if they could be given training and help)? Would health workers wish them to do more?

Training in providing health services

• Do teachers' colleges and colleges of health (which train community health workers) need to think again about their training concerning providing health services in schools?

Can external agencies help?

• What may be the role of external bodies such as international agencies and large non-governmental organizations (such as *Save the Children*) in providing school health services?

The need for simple guidelines

• What simple guidelines exist to help schools who wish to provide better health services? Could new guidelines or checklists (such as those on page 150) be produced and used?

Monitoring and evaluating the provision of health services

• How can we find out how well we are cooperating together and providing health services? How could we provide them better?

IDEAS FOR

POLICY MAKERS AND PROGRAMME DESIGNERS

● It is necessary to develop a national policy which recognizes the need for local action and supports it.

● We must seek a national consensus on the nature and need for health promotion.

● Once projects at local and school level have proved the value of comprehensive school health promotion, the ideas can spread. However, they are most likely to be effective if they spread gradually, and if they are based on the interest and enthusiasm of schools and local areas.

PROGRAMME PLANNERS, MANAGERS AND TRAINERS

● The need to:
  make sure that projects are only launched if schools and communities understand and will support them;
  clarify the project goals and derive objectives from them;
  set objectives for each stage and break these down into tasks;
  match resources to these tasks;
  bear in mind that different schools will approach the task of health promotion in different ways.

● Evaluation is an ongoing activity which must be planned from the outset of the project. It is essential for effective project planning and management.

SCHOOL AND COMMUNITY

● Careful planning at school and classroom level is the foundation of all good health-promotion programmes.

● All planning needs to list different tasks and needs to be discussed fully with teachers and, where necessary, with the community.

● Priority health themes need to be selected for school and class. They should not be too many. They should complement rather than replace content officially recommended in the school syllabus.

CHAPTER 7

Planning Action at Local Level

Part 1: Project Planning

• Different levels of planning • Locally based planning supported by national policy • Decisions necessary before starting a new project • Deciding on the aims and purpose of a project • Project objectives and tasks linked to them • Linking tasks to resources and deriving a timetable for action

The need for planning

Every country makes some provision at national level for health action in its schools. Most local areas identify health needs and, on different occasions, they involve schools in programmes and campaigns to meet them. Nearly all schools undertake some health action. Often such activities take place regularly. Health topics are included in the curriculum; national and local events such as World AIDS Day and Road Safety weeks are organized yearly. At school level children are encouraged to keep clean and are given responsibility to clean their school. Attempts are made to improve school feeding and to promote food cleanliness. Often these activities are carefully planned, though usually separately by different people. They are all valuable.

In this chapter we look at the possibility of bringing all these actions together into one agreed plan – in other words, planning the development of health-promoting schools.

Levels of planning

Such planning may begin from an individual **school** and spread to others, be launched by a small project at **local level** involving a number of schools, or even in rare cases originate from a **national** or **provincial** programme. In every case cooperation between all three levels is essential.

National policy supporting local action

In chapters 1 and 2 we made a case for a national commitment to the principle of comprehensive health promotion in schools; for a national 'entitlement' of what schools should provide and for a national policy which supports individual school and community initiatives. As yet few countries have such comprehensive planning at national level. But even where no such policy exists it is very likely that an approach by a local project or even an individual school will be welcomed, provided it is made sensibly and tactfully.

Thank you so much for your suggestions on our project. We won't let you down.

Why locally based planning is necessary

Even when there is total national support for the idea of school health action, the largest part of any planning still needs to take place at local level. There are two reasons for this.

● **Local needs**
Every local context, every school, every year is different. Even in cases where schools nationwide share common problems such as threats from AIDS or pollution, the understanding and impact of these problems on communities differs widely.

● **Local ownership**
The success of a local project depends almost entirely on its acceptance and support by the school and its wider community. The great majority of the activities in a health-promoting school are community related. Many of them require an extra investment of time by different people, including parents and children as well as teachers. Unless there is a general *and continuing* agreement that these activities are worthwhile (because they make the children healthier, and are likely to help their school performance) then there is little chance of the project making a real impact.

Locally based projects

By far the largest number of attempts to develop health-promoting schools are to be found in small projects involving groups of schools. Small projects 'take off' for a number of reasons. Some reasons are excellent. Organizers may genuinely believe that they have local support, and that they can make an impact and can promote community health. In other cases the motives are mixed. Sometimes a group, often with outside help, organizes a project more for its own purposes than for the help of the community and may well assume or report support which is not really there. Often such projects make quite heavy demands on schools and teachers. Few survive the departure of their organizers.

Before we start a project we need to ask ourselves a few questions. Unless the answers to most of these are 'Yes' we should think again before starting.

THE 'YES' TEST

1. Are we, ourselves, completely convinced of the importance of school health action as part of every school's programme?

2. Would we keep on supporting it even if *no* extra resources were available to help it happen?

3. Are we confident that we can get enough 'people that matter' to share our view?

4. Do we believe that we can get at least some schools to support 'giving it a try', without offering them extra incentives beyond those such as in-service training and resource materials which any new programme has a right to expect?

5. Do we understand and accept:

i. that the programme *does* involve teachers in acquiring new knowledge and ways of working with children, parents and health workers;

ii. that it *should not* ask them to do things which are beyond the energy they have;

iii. that we need, therefore, to modify the demands we make to suit what the schools wish to do and are prepared to do.

6. Do we hope and expect that the approaches and practices will still be found in the school in ten years' time and that they will have spread to other schools?

Assuming that our project has passed the 'Yes' test, let us now look at some of the different stages in project planning.

The tasks of planning

There are six important tasks in the planning process.

- Decide on the **purpose** of the project and deriving aims or general objectives.

- Set **objectives** for each stage of the project.

- List the **tasks** to be undertaken for each objective.

- Assess the **resources** necessary for the project as a whole and for the different tasks identified.

- Set the objectives, tasks and resources, where possible, within a **time plan.**

PURPOSE

▽

General objectives

▽

Project objectives

▽

Tasks

▽

Resources

▽

Time plan

Purpose → Objectives

The first step is to clarify in the minds of those who seek to initiate the project what the aim and purpose of the project is. Very often at this stage we can find that there are different dreams, ideas and even definitions of health among those who wish to set up the project. It is essential that all share common goals.

It is also important that when aims are drawn up they are stated in clear and simple terms. 'Technical planning' language, using terms such as 'infrastructure' or 'input/output relationships', may sound good but often it draws a curtain between plans and the real world.

Here is a slightly adapted version of a list drawn up in 1991 at an international workshop in Nairobi, where project workers met to exchange ideas. They were working with Health Action Schools, using the Child-to-Child approach in four different African countries.

HEALTH ACTION SCHOOLS USING THE CHILD-TO-CHILD APPROACH

Statement of purpose

To help primary schools become places where good health is practised and from which good health is promoted for the benefit of the communities they serve. Health is defined as involving all aspects of physical, mental, emotional and environmental health, with a first emphasis on prevention.

Aims For the staff and school

▤ to improve and encourage the improvement of the health and well-being of the children and staff in their schools, their families and the local community;

▤ to forge close links with health workers, health centres and health-promotion activities in the community;

▤ to involve parents more closely as partners in school/family health activities;

▤ to strengthen relationships between children;

▤ to use active teaching methods which develop life skills;

▤ to have a health plan linked to important health topics (in the same way as they have a timetable or set of school rules).

Aims for the children

▤ to spread health messages and good health practices from school to home;

▤ to learn and practise good health knowledge and skills and develop caring attitudes NOW which they carry forward to the next generation;

▤ to develop the ability to take wise decisions about their own health and where possible about the health of others.

At this first stage it is also important to be aware of the problems, present and potential, which will form the background to the programme. Such problems are often great but unless we face realities our programme may look good on paper but prove unrealistic in practice. One useful technique is to 'brainstorm' and list these problems, possibly on a blackboard or a large piece of paper, and then divide them into groups and decide how many of them would raise difficulties and which others might be helped by the project.

Objectives for each stage → Tasks → Resources

The next stage in the planning process is to list the **objectives for each stage** of the project, and under each to list the different **tasks** involved, linking them to the **resources** available.

Below we shall outline some of the likely objectives and tasks related to a small project.

Planning a project

OBJECTIVES AND TASKS	LESSONS FROM EXPERIENCE
1. Establish the need for the programme and ensure potential support for it TASKS: ▪ Clarify goals ▪ Contact national authorities to obtain agreement and support ▪ Make a budget. Ensure minimum funding is available ▪ Make sure of your own commitment (apply the 'Yes' test) ▪ Obtain support at local level	• Involve as many persons as possible in goal clarification. This ensures wide ownership of the project. A national seminar producing an agreed statement of intent would be very valuable. • Approach aid agencies and large NGOs: they might fund such a seminar and agree to fund materials for the programme. • Be sure to involve both education and health sectors from the outset.
2. Set up mechanisms to organize the project TASKS: ▪ Establish a project committee and specify its role ▪ Agree coordination mechanisms at school level ▪ Consider methods of evaluation	• Ensure your committee is small and can meet frequently. Education and health interests must be represented. • Apply yourselves to evaluation design right from the start. Possibly involve the local teachers' college in this task.
3. To clarify relations and linkages TASKS: ▪ Check that links are made between national and local levels and between education and health	• Reporting progress and making links takes time and is frequently neglected. It is so much easier to 'get on with the job' at local level. But it is vital to a project's success to remain constantly in the mind of national authorities. • Media coverage always helps.

OBJECTIVES AND TASKS	LESSONS FROM EXPERIENCE
4. Find out about the local situation (general) TASKS: ▨ Assess local needs as stated by community ▨ Consult local medical records ▨ Become aware of traditional beliefs and practices	• There may not be a need for any sophisticated research here. • A carefully chosen local group may be able to able to give guidance at a carefully prepared day seminar. • Simple techniques of need analysis for groups exist. Agencies such as UNICEF can advise and might provide a facilitator.
5. Set objectives for the project and decide on criteria to be applied to its evaluation TASKS: ▨ Discuss desirable goals ▨ Set realistic objectives ▨ Link these with evaluation	• Objectives should emphasise that although some content and approaches need to be followed by all schools, a major aim of the project is to develop individual action and decision-making by each school. There should be a clear distinction between minimum objectives and desirable objectives. After each objective, a statement needs to be added, headed 'How do we know how far we have met it?'
6. Agree a curriculum framework for the schools, acceptable within the national framework but reflecting local priorities, and allowing for local variations between schools TASKS: ▨ Review the current curriculum ▨ Draw up a simple outline for the project ▨ Check with national level to ensure that the proposals are agreeable ▨ Inform and discuss with local inspectors and supervisors to ensure that they are aware and approve of the action	• The document drawn up might contain: i. Minimum health content needed by all children. (A brief list of topics with reference to *Children for Health*.) ii. Recommended methodologies to be used by all schools. iii. An analysis of those topics already covered in current school syllabuses with suggestions on how these could be rearranged. iv. Guidance on how these and additional topics can be integrated within the school or class 'health themes' chosen by each school (not more than one or two per term). v. Suggestions on how schools may be able to assess changes in children's health knowledge, attitudes and practice.

OBJECTIVES AND TASKS	LESSONS FROM EXPERIENCE
7. Assess resources needed for the project and ensure that they are available TASKS: ▦ Draw up a minimum resources list for the project as a whole ▦ Ensure that each time a task is undertaken, necessary resources are identified and secured ▦ If minimum resources are not available the task needs to be rethought	● Four kinds of resources need to be considered: people; money; materials and time. ● If possible ensure that at the beginning of the programme someone is given the time and responsibility to coordinate activities and motivate schools. Such a person could be seconded from normal duties, as a teacher, trainer or inspector, either full- or part-time. Without such support at the beginning, a programme risks getting off to a shaky start. ● By contrast avoid making big material inputs into a project. This may lead to difficulties when the ideas are spread to many schools.
8. Select areas and schools TASKS: ▦ Establish criteria ▦ Select schools ▦ Ensure that the selection is agreeable to local authorities  *Additional, but not representative.*	● The criteria for selection might be as follows: i. The head and teachers wish to take on the programme. ii. The schools should be easy to reach by the organizers. iii. They should be close to each other so that they could act as a support. iv. They should be reasonably representative of schools in the area (sometimes it is useful to use high-cost schools as additions to a project rather than as part of the main sample).
9. Further analyse the context TASKS: ▦ Ensure schools identify needs and priorities relevant to their own specific situation	● Once the schools are chosen, each school needs to meet with local parents and community leaders to discuss the priorities identified by the project and to add in what they consider to be any important local priorities. ● Don't forget to ask children. Their views are valuable.

OBJECTIVES AND TASKS	LESSONS FROM EXPERIENCE
10. Plan the project and its monitoring TASKS: ▨ Draw up a work plan in as much detail as possible (but leaving some flexibility) ▨ Draw up a parallel plan for monitoring/evaluation	• Plan the first year in considerable detail, on a month-by-month basis. At this stage it is important to collect baseline data for evaluation. • This can be done with the cooperation of each of the schools, by filling in a simple 'healthy school' checklist. Samples of children and teachers in each school could take part in a health knowledge quiz (including some practical questions).
11. Ensure that each school produces its own action plan TASK: ▨ As above (also see the example on page 150)	• Arrange a seminar and assist schools in drawing up plans. • Also suggest: i. they consider drawing up a set of health rules as part of their general school rules; ii. that they establish health committees; iii. that they consider the role of out-of-school activities in promoting health and links with communities.
12. Conduct a programme of awareness raising and initial training TASKS: ▨ Ensure widest publicity ▨ Plan initial training course ▨ Run initial course for teachers ▨ Run additional course for heads and health coordinators (See Chapter 9 for suggestions for planning and conducting courses.)	• Children are a programme's most powerful advocates. In many countries they have their own radio or television programme to show what they have achieved though health action programmes.

Making an impact.

OBJECTIVES AND TASKS	LESSONS FROM EXPERIENCE
13. Launch the project TASKS: ▨ Ensure both local and national authorities are aware that the project is recognized as a part of educational policy	● Health projects are vote winners. Aim high when asking prominent people to open courses. Ministers themselves may agree to come, which ensures official support and media coverage. ● Be sure to ask prominent persons from both health and education sectors.
14. Monitor and support it carefully TASKS: ▨ Ensure that the project is carefully monitored, particularly in its initial stages ▨ Act immediately to give clarification and support where it is needed. Change practice where necessary ▨ Ensure that schools themselves monitor their own activities	● Remember that keeping up a project is difficult. There has to be evidence that the activities are worth the effort put in. Hence when plans prove too ambitious they must be modified. ● Experience suggests that, more than anything, the enthusiasm shown by children helps to motivate the teachers and parents to continue new activities. As time goes on the activities become established and thus easier to maintain. ● It may also become possible to show the heads that their efforts are really making a difference, particularly through increases in attendance rates and through parents' reactions concerning the behaviour of their children.
15. Arrange for frequent sharing and discussion between those involved TASK: ▨ As above	● Health coordinators in schools need to be given an opportunity to meet regularly, preferably visiting each other's schools. ● A competition for a 'Healthy School Shield' could be organized.
16. Modify activities as a result of experience gained	

Objectives/tasks→Work plan

Every project needs a work plan divided into months to ensure that stages and tasks are undertaken in time and in sequence. Shorter-term planning needs to be done week by week. Drawing up a work plan is difficult and project workers will need help. Often it is useful to work back from the date the project needs to start in schools (usually at the beginning of a school year) in order to find out when to schedule the various tasks and thus find out when it will necessary to start the planning process.

Part 2: Planning for a single school

> • Single schools making their own plans • Stages in school-based planning • Planning at classroom level • Monitoring and evaluation of local and school-based projects

The idea of the health-promoting school depends, as its name suggests, on each school making its own health plan. Even when small local projects are organized, such as that just described, each school within the project will have a different approach and different priorities. But quite often individual schools become interested in making their own plans to become health promoting. Often these are schools with considerable local support and some access to funds. The stages and examples below provide a possible sequence of activities relevant not only to one school starting out on its own to develop a comprehensive health plan but also to a school operating alongside within a small project.

Stages in school-based planning
(with some suggestions)

1. Assess interest and enlist support.
  • Who wants it?
  • Ask yourself:
  Do you really believe the idea will make a difference to the school?
  Have you enough support on your side?
  Can you count on it?

2. Clarify relations with local organizers (particularly if the school is part of a wider project) and with advisers and managers.
  • Make sure that everyone who needs to know understands about the new ideas you are introducing.

3. Agree objectives, components and responsibilities for health promotion activities. Set up a health committee if necessary. Make a simple chart or plan of tasks and responsibilities.

● Take plenty of time discussing this with the staff and listen particularly to their fears about being asked to do too much. Appoint at least two teachers (to support each other) as health coordinators. Don't forget to involve parents and children as part of the school health committee. Involve the health worker from the start, particularly in drawing up a simple set of health rules for the school.

4. Agree action to improve the health environment of the school and to provide health services in consultation with local health workers (see Chapter 6).

● Why not hold a working group (all volunteers) to include staff, the local health worker and some interested parents on the subject 'School health services – what can we all do to help?' Perhaps a member of the national school health education programme would agree to act as organizer.

5. Agree a 'working curriculum for the school' which would be compatible with the current health education content of the official school curriculum.

● Analyse the current school curriculum to find out what health topics were already taught and decide if others should be added.

● Appoint a working group of teachers to discuss and agree school health themes and priorities and to decide which classes would concentrate on special action projects. School themes will almost certainly include hygiene, safety and nutrition.

6. Agree health-action topics for each class, and how these would fit into school themes. If other health content exists in the school syllabus which has to be covered, also plan where this needs to fit in. If the school plan suggests teaching health topics in a different order from that prescribed, it may be wise to obtain agreement either from national authorities or the local inspector.

● Here is one alternative: each class from 4-8 would take two health-action themes (one each in the first two terms). The last term would be kept free for teaching health topics (such as the human skeleton), which are in the official syllabus but not in the health plan. Health-action themes would include one school theme and one theme especially chosen for each class[1] as follows:

---

[1] Some schools might prefer to have a new theme every six weeks thus, covering more topics.

> **CLASSES 1-2**
> Keeping clean, Safety at home, Our food.
>
> **CLASS 3**
> (1) Clean safe water (2) Worms
>
> **CLASS 4**
> (1) Road safety (2) Insect-born diseases (including malaria)
>
> **CLASS 5**
> (1) Food hygiene (2) Child growth
>
> **CLASS 6**
> (1) Food for the family (2) Immunization
>
> **CLASS 7**
> (1) Disability (2) AIDS
>
> **CLASS 8**
> (1) Substance abuse (2) Our bodies growing and changing

7. Agree how health action around the school is to be managed and monitored by the children. What would be the duties of any children's health committee or similar body, or of class health-monitors? Would there be any form of 'twinning system' (older with younger children); or any out-of-class activities such as clubs, health scouts, or 'health messengers' to the community?

- See suggestions made in Chapter 5.

- Make sure that as many children as possible are given *real* responsibility. If you expect a lot from them they will usually live up to your expectations.

8. Decide on any school/community events which might be organized during the year, and how far the school might cooperate in national events and campaigns.

- Events could include a school Health Fair or participation in a national event such as World AIDS Day. Remember that such events are extremely valuable but also very time-consuming, and they should not be organized too often. Children, especially in a school health club, should be involved in organization and given responsibility.

9. Decide what training and resource material is necessary and possible.

- Training is discussed in the next chapter. It is vital, and help should be sought to organize it. It should be ongoing. A vital aspect of training is making sure that the teachers have the right health messages themselves. Reference materials such as *Facts for Life*, *Children for Health*, or the Child-to-Child resource books are thus vital. Every attempt should also be made to see that teachers *really consult* these books. Quizzes and competitions help here.

10. Decide how all the activities would be monitored and evaluated during, and at the end of, the year. Who would do it?

● Chapter 9 describes this in more detail. It would be valuable to have both inside and outside monitoring for a school programme – both to see how well it was working and to assess what changes it had been able to make. It might be possible to find a health tutor in a local college, or a member of the national school health service, who was prepared to help.

● The school can, however, help to monitor its own progress by using checklists such as the one on page 150. A school/community health group might be set up and meet each term to discuss what had been planned and what had been achieved. Children can also test each other. One suggestion could be to design a local health-competency test (administered by the children), leading to the award of a 'health badge'. They could retake the quiz (like a driving test).

Third Time Healthy!

Planning at classroom level

Even if schools do not have a school plan to become 'health promoting' individual teachers can still add in some of the ideas to their work.

If there *is* a school plan, class teachers must still make a scheme for the units they cover. This is easier in the first classes of the basic education cycle where teachers tend to be class teachers. Later, since teachers teach subjects rather than classes, more discussion becomes necessary between teachers. In each case it will be necessary to do certain things:

Make a year plan by dividing the teaching into units. In the school we have described above the teacher's grade 6 year plan for health might look like this:

TERM 1
Food for the family (school theme)

TERM 2
Immunization (special theme), including 'immunization day' for parents

TERM 3
Regular syllabus topics, plus preparation for school fair on safety

Under each of the special themes teachers will need to decide:

1. What are the main objectives; e.g. What does the teacher want the class to be able to *know* and *do* and *feel* at the end of the six-week period? (This sounds more difficult than it is. Often the objectives will be clearly set out by the government or in documents such as *Children for Health*. The teacher will only have to decide how far these suit the age and experience of the class.)

Remember: always set reasonable targets and try to state the objectives in a way that makes it easy to see whether you have achieved them or not.

2. How many lessons will be needed to put across and confirm the main ideas? (A teacher cannot expect to have more than one period a week and often may have less.)

3. How should the unit be sequenced so that the four steps discussed on page 40 can be covered? What should pupils be expected to do between lessons in their families and communities?

4. How can the unit be supported across the curriculum in other classes?

5. What outcomes can be expected (especially if children are going to show these to other classes or to parents)?

6. How can we find out what children have learnt or how they have changed?

EXAMPLE: CLASS UNIT ON IMMUNIZATION (CLASS 6)

Objectives:

Children know and understand:
- that all children need to be protected against killer diseases during the first year of a child's life (list the diseases);
- why failing to immunize (or failing to complete the course of immunization) is so dangerous;
- when and how to obtain immunization.

Children know how to:
- record immunizations of their family and neighbours;
- find out why people do not immunize their children;
- spread immunization messages to others (and help when they take children to the clinic).

Children develop attitudes:
- ... of concern for those who have not had children immunized.

Five lessons with home activities in between
1. Understanding about immunization (find out about immunization in our families).
2. Dangers of not immunizing; and why children are not immunized (survey of knowledge and attitudes to immunization).
3. Discussion of survey; planning how children can help to spread messages (children prepare own plays, posters, songs).
4. Discussion of work prepared and planning for 'immunization day': immunization day for parents (Saturday).
5. Feedback from immunization day.

Activities across the curriculum (often involving collaboration between teachers)
1. Story telling and writing based on the book, *Diseases Defeated* (Language).
2. Making graphs of immunizations in 'our families' (Maths).
3. Discussing the role of the health service in preventing disease (Social studies).
4. How our bodies protect us against disease (Science).
5. Designing posters and making immunization games (Art/Craft).

Outputs expected on the 'immunization day' for parents
1. Talk from a health worker.
2. Songs and plays performed by children.
3. Demonstration of posters (children talk about them).
4. Talk by a parent.
5. Offer by children to help remind families, and help when immunizations are due (children give parents immunization cards they have produced).

Monitoring and evaluation of activities at project and school level

Chapter 9, 'Making a difference', will emphasize that the purpose of monitoring evaluation is to help us to do things better and that the process of evaluation needs to start right from the beginning of an activity. It is essential to remember that the most important evaluators are *we* who are involved in planning and implementing the programme. *We* see it developing. *We* can judge whether things are going well or badly, what needs strengthening and what needs changing. The more of *us* there are, involved in the planning process, the more *we* are consulted, the more *we* are committed, the more chance *we* will have of shaping the project to meet *our* needs.

One thing is certain. Projects and the schools which form part of them are living things. They grow and change and adapt. If they do not do so, or if our plans do not expect them to do so, something is seriously wrong.

Part 3: Moving on from small projects

- Why rapid, nationwide dissemination from small projects may not work ● Two ways in which a more gradual spread can be managed

Mass replication of 'health-promoting school' projects may be dangerous

Once a smaller 'health-action school' project has proved its worth, all would hope the ideas to spread further. This can lead towards greater success but if implementation is attempted too quickly and too uniformly there is grave danger.

As we have seen, the effectiveness of the 'health-promoting school' idea depends on schools and communities *understanding it, wanting to do it* and feeling they *'own' it*. Governments and large international aid agencies like to evolve big programmes very quickly from small prototypes. They have a phrase – 'going to scale' – which is sometimes interpreted as reproducing one model all over a country or region. This kind of policy will not work in relation to health-promoting schools, since the desire to be 'health promoting' must come from within the school and community and not from outside it.

Two ways in which good practice *can* spread

1. The **first** of these ways is gradually to widen the number of health-promoting schools year by year. Of course some of the original schools in a project will lose interest but if many retain it and can show benefits the door is open for the number to grow. Schools and groups of schools can 'opt in' to the group until gradually the numbers grow large. At last it may be possible within a district or region for communities, local education and health workers, and even parents to *expect* a school to be health promoting. Perhaps schools opting to being part of a 'health action' network might be asked to agree to meet a number of conditions of criteria. Here is a list of eleven.

All health-action schools in our area should have

- A school health committee
- Two coordinating health teachers with full support from the head
- Children involved in health action outside class
- Evidence of regular health services (such as identifying children who are unwell, weak or unhappy) coming from both *outside* and *inside* the school
- Regular checks to improve the hygiene and sanitation of the school
- Regular monitoring of the food brought, supplied, and sold to children
- A good safety programme
- A plan which identifies health priorities on a monthly, termly or yearly basis; sets objectives to meet them; and tries to find out whether these have been met
- At least one school event a year which involves the parents in health action
- A sense of responsibility among children and teachers to help others, prevent ill health, and reduce illness and absenteeism in the school
- Pride in the health record and health actions of their school

---

2. The **second** way is to introduce the changes gradually into the national system. Here are a few steps:

- The definition of comprehensive school health in national policy
- The concept of health priorities, local as well as national, as part of the school curriculum
- A recommendation to set up school health committees in an area, with suggestions of what these committees might do
- Local or national school hygiene composition with special marks to reward the regular participation of children
- Positive encouragement of Child-to-Child activities

... and so on gradually until all the 'pieces' of the 'action school' fall into place.

QUESTIONS FOR EVERYONE

Getting local level projects started?

• How can the interest and demand for health-promoting or health-action schools at local level be identified and stimulated?

• How can local people be persuaded to identify their own priorities, organize their own programmes and build up their own partnerships within the communities?

• How can realistic minimum resources (especially people) be identified and assured?

• Who can best support the projects and in what way?

Learning to plan effectively?

• How can we help those who *want* to create projects, develop schools and plan programmes, to do it well?

• How can we ensure that what they are planning is realistic and likely to be supported?

• What help can they get from outside which does not make it difficult for the ideas to spread (once outside help is no longer there)?

Supporting them. . . so that they grow strong

• How can projects and schools be helped and encouraged to grow, develop and change after the first enthusiasm has worn off?

• How can schools and projects be organized to help and encourage each other?

Moving on

• How can plans to extend these ideas and practices be worked into programmes from the start?

• How can new practice within small projects be looked at and discussed by others, so that they can make useful decisions about spreading further?

IDEAS FOR

 ## POLICY MAKERS

- Developing 'health-promoting colleges' alongside 'health-promoting schools'
- A new look at in-service education as wider than just courses for teachers, to include:
  - the exchange of ideas between programmes, schools and teachers, through visits and discussion
  - joint production of materials
  - cooperative learning

 ## PROGRAMME DESIGNERS

The need to design programmes for health-promoting colleges
- Planning health across the college curriculum
- Identifying carrier subjects including education theory, child development and educational psychology
- Integrating health-including life skills into subject teaching methods
- Linking colleges with groups of schools
  - ☐ Schools can serve as a resource for students, for research, for evaluation and for practical teaching in health
  - ☐ Colleges can serve as a resource for schools, in sharing ideas and materials, in access to resource materials and in advice

 ## LOCAL PLANNERS, MANAGERS AND TRAINERS

- Effective planning for courses is essential for their success. Courses must have clear objectives and manageable programmes. There needs to be special emphasis on the involvement of children in courses.
- In addition to courses, local in-service programmes need to include alternative ways of sharing new knowledge and new methods

 ## SCHOOL AND COMMUNITY

- School-based training is central to the improvement of knowledge and skills in health education

Organizing Training

> • Who needs what kind of training for school health promotion?
> • Planning health promotion through health-promoting colleges
> • Links between colleges and schools • Courses for teachers and how
> to organize them • Other ways of in-service training through
> discussion, visits, planning and writing together; also through
> guided reading and school-based seminars

Needs

Effective health promotion in schools will be difficult to achieve without proper training of all those involved. We are asking many people to acquire new knowledge, to take on new ways of thinking, to practise new methods, to trust and cooperate with different sets of people and to change their attitudes towards health in schools.

Who needs what kind of training?

At national level we need programmes to raise the awareness of policy makers and programme planners. Without their understanding and commitment there will be no effective comprehensive health promotion programme.

Once programmes are set up, we need to orient the programme planners, the trainers, the project managers and the evaluators. In order that their work is understood and accepted, we need to include other members of the community in the training – such as school inspectors, school managers, parents and community leaders. Experience suggests they greatly welcome this and that quite apart from the knowledge they gain, involving them helps to ensure their cooperation.

The largest group of those who need training are certainly those who work directly in and with schools: the heads, the teachers and the local health workers.

Training of trainers

Training of trainers involves particular problems in planning courses. Often those who organize them are 'experts', sometimes even from outside the system in which they are working. They may have quite rigid views of the 'right way' to organize a programme.

There are therefore six essential DOs and one very definite DON'T for those involved in the organization of such training.

DO

● **Identify core material** which trainers agree to use as a basis both for their own course and as a resource for later training. Such material may well include this book, *Children for Health*, *Helping Health Workers Learn* (Werner and Bower), and, if available, the *Training Pack* issued by the Child-to-Child Trust and available from them.

● **Agree definitions** of comprehensive school health promotion and education, and agree that these will be used throughout the training; on the basis of this set and agree objectives for the training.

● Ensure that **the context** in which the training is taking place is carefully analysed. Such analysis could include current health priorities, and educational policies and practice, so that any training planned will be both acceptable and possible.

● Organize any training so that it **generates materials** which can later be used as tools for training at other levels, e.g. training hand-outs, check-lists, course plans, evaluation instruments.

● Use **methods and approaches which are a model** both for subsequent training but also for action in class and at school/community level. Thus training needs to encourage **active participation** at all times.

● Remember that **training cannot be achieved through one single course** or seminar (though it may be started with one), but must continue through a variety of ways, see page 133.

DON'T

● Promote rigid 'How to Do It' programmes which deny local trainers the initiative to plan their own courses to meet their own needs.

No training at this level is likely to be successful unless there is a firm basis of medical support. Trainers *must* be aware of how they can get up-to-date health information to support their training. In addition to health education personnel it will be important to have a doctor (preferably a paediatrician) as a member of the course team and to make sure that all the trainers have at least read the up-to-date information in *Children for Health*.

Comprehensive health promotion in teachers' colleges

When we talk of new approaches to health promotion we think of changing the behaviour of heads and senior teachers in schools. But it is equally important to reach young teachers when they undertake their first training.

For this reason colleges which train teachers need to develop as models of comprehensive health promotion in just the same way as schools do.

They need to:

- Understand what health and health promotion are and why it is important.
- Develop policies towards effective provision of health services *by* the college as well as *for* the college; towards good management of hygiene and nutrition; and towards the teaching and learning of health education using effective, active methods.
- Plan an effective college curriculum which identifies core subjects such as environmental science and which introduces health knowledge and life skills. Train students in the skills of 'health across the curriculum'. Health content and approaches, including the Child-to-Child approach, need to be infused into 'education' subjects such as principles of education, child development and educational psychology.
- Students in college need to learn to take responsibility in the college and to take action in the community at their own level (probably based around the identification of priority themes).

When this happens, as in colleges in Uganda and Zambia, it can be very effective, since colleges often have resources that are denied primary schools.

In our colleges we are organized into health action teams. We made a nursery for fruit trees.

The immunization clinic is located in our college. Students help to organize it and the records.

Our college organizes a health theatre group which plays in the villages.

Colleges and schools associated with them

One of the most effective ways of organizing a 'healthy schools' project and at the same time providing training for college students, is to associate a group of 'health-action schools' with a college. Here is a shortened version of a report made in 1992 when representatives from four African countries (Kenya, Uganda, Sierra Leone and Zambia) met to discuss health-action projects which had started in these countries.

THE COLLEGES AND ASSOCIATED SCHOOLS

The college role in planning and coordinating action

School action plans are often (but not always) made in conjunction with colleges. In each case the college needs to look on itself as a facilitator of what individual schools want to do, and as helping in the exchange of ideas between schools.

Monitoring and evaluating impact

Colleges can monitor schools using simple instruments locally developed. They can also study the longer-term impact of the new approaches on the knowledge and skills of children. In these ways students can gain practical experience in evaluation.

Students as observers in practical teaching

During their teaching practice, student teachers need to:
● observe and record health teaching and health activities taking place in associated schools;
● practise manageable activities through topics which can be planned and executed within a two- or three-week period;
● discuss possible follow-up activities with the class teacher.

The college as a resource centre for schools

The college can:
● keep resource books on health and health education and lend them to teachers;
● organize writing workshops so that teachers in schools can make lesson plans, activity sheets and story books for use in schools;
● act as a 'bank' for collecting songs, plays and stories, and records of activities undertaken by different schools, so that these ideas can be preserved and shared;
● organize exhibitions of materials made in the schools, and arrange concerts in which drama and songs created in the schools can be performed.

In-service education (1): courses for teachers

When new programmes are launched the most common way of training is through organizing courses for those who are about to start them. Such courses are usually held at a local centre and last for a few days. As the number of schools beginning 'health action programmes' increases, so the experience of designing courses for them builds up. Here are some of the lessons from experience.

Who attends?

• Each school involved should send two or more teachers from the same school as the new approaches demand great change. Teachers need to support each other.

• Heads are vital to the success of health-promotion programmes. They need to attend at least part of every course. The same applies to local level inspectors in education and to local health workers.

• When community members such as chairmen or chairwomen of parent/teachers' associations attend, courses will benefit greatly.

• Children make all the difference to a course. They should be included in the sessions such as those on methodology and those identifying needs and priorities in families, not just invited to perform songs and dances at the opening ceremony. Once participants realize how much children can do and how creative they can be it will change their attitude.

• Make use of the course to raise interest and gain publicity for the programme. Thus design the opening or closing, so that it can be of interest to community leaders, the press or the radio.

• Try to mix health and education workers and design programmes so that they can share ideas.

The programme

When organizing a programme start by remembering two important 'DON'Ts' They are:

1. Don't overload it.

Teach a limited amount thoroughly. Health ideas are difficult and challenging. Make sure teachers are given plenty of time to understand them. If they are only half-understood, ideas are not likely to survive.

2. Don't build your programmes around talks and lectures.

In fact have as few of these as you possibly can. Participants learn by doing not listening.

Here are just a few DOs which have not yet been mentioned but which are important.

1. DO ensure that the **atmosphere** of the course is pleasant and friendly, that those attending enjoy it and that they are comfortable and have good food. Otherwise they will not cooperate, neither will they be prepared to take steps forward towards change.

2. DO set clear **objectives** for the course that can be achieved, and make sure that everyone knows and understands what they are and what they mean. Display them and refer back to them frequently. Make sure that they are referred to when the course is evaluated.

3. DO make sure that there are enough good and useable **resource materials** available for participants and that they know how to use them. One of the most important functions of a course is always to show teachers where they can find the help they need when they start putting ideas into practice.

4. DO use **methods** in the course that you would expect the participants to use in their schools and communities. Good practices are more easily 'caught' than 'taught'. Lectures about activity methods get nobody anywhere.

5. DO make sure that a large part of the course is taken up with participants **developing plans and materials** which they will be able to use in their schools soon after the course has finished.

6. DO involve **health workers** and **community members** alongside teachers in courses.

7. DO always **include children** in courses, not just to perform at the opening ceremony but as a resource for sessions on methodology. These sessions need to concentrate on demonstrating how children can think, act, plan and create – using their own initiative, not just following instructions from adults.

'Do you really mean they made all this in one afternoon?'

On the next page we give one example of what a programme for a four-day course might look like. We assume it is organized for 30 participants from five schools and their communities in a local project such as that described in Chapter 8.

PROGRAMME FOR A FOUR DAY COURSE

	DAY 1	DAY 2	DAY 3	DAY 4
A.M. 1	Opening and discussion of course objectives. Participants choose an evaluation group to monitor how far the course meets the set objectives.	Two health priorities chosen by the group are presented and discussed. Resource material, e.g. *Children for Health* identified. Objectives set. Group identify what action children and communities can take.	Two further health priorities are discussed. Both this session and the session on Day 2 are led by a doctor from the local hospital working together with a health educator.	Introduction to making action plans followed by schools discussing and presenting plans. Among the items to be discussed in school groups are: 1. Who will be responsible; 2. Setting up committees; 3. Setting objectives; 4. Number of themes identified; 5. The school environment; 6. Involvement of children in health action; 7. Health services in and for school; 8. Evaluation.
A.M. 2	The idea of comprehensive school health promotion. Discussion of what it means, programmes in school and links with the communities.	Methods and approaches; (1): general. Examines the active four-stage approach discussed in Chapter 3, linking learning with action. Exercises linking this approach with health themes discussed earlier.	Practical work in school groups. Preparing one unit with children. Each school selects one health topic for one class drawn from one of the four themes presented earlier. They plan a sequence of lessons and out-of-class activities round this theme and develop at least one of the activities with a group of children.	Doing it better. Discuss simple evaluation at school level, including that done by children. Amend and agree a simple checklist prepared by course team.
P.M. 1	Looking at resource materials. Examining the materials. Exercises on how to use them.	Methods and approaches **(2)**. Divide into three groups of 10. Each group discusses and itself practises one of three methods: story telling, drama and surveys.		Agreement of a time-table for the next three months. Discussion of course evaluation. Summary and closing of the course.
P.M. 2	Assessing needs and priorities. Choosing and discussing both learning needs and health needs.	Activities outside the classroom, also in three groups of 10 which report on: Group 1 – health committees; group 2 – healthy school environment; group 3 – children's action (clubs, scouts, pairing).	Presentation of the units to the whole course. A list of criteria has been drawn up. Among these is an assessment of how far children's activities have led them to think and create rather than to follow instructions.	

In-service education (2):
other types of in-service training

Although most training still takes place through courses, the most common ways of learning new skills and changing practice happen on the job.

Here are just a few ways in which we can learn:

• By visiting each other and working together

We gain from seeing other's ideas at work. At the same time if we know that someone is coming to visit our school or our programme we are bound to want to show them interesting things we have done. If, perhaps, we all agree a *list of points to look for*, this will motivate us even further.

• Help on the job

Although visits from 'experts' of one type or another can be helpful, the most important helpers are people with the same background and experience as those they are helping. That is why appointing and training advisory teachers in schools or groups of schools works so well.

• Planning and writing together

If groups of teachers and health workers can come together to make useful materials for use in schools, they can learn from this experience and share ideas informally while they are working together. Such materials could include:

- Action plans for school, or campaigns such as Road Safety Day
- Lesson or unit plans
- Activity sheets
- Suggestions for drama and songs
- Write-ups of activities done by schools
- Plans for radio programmes
- Collections of children's work, e.g. for a poster competition
- Checklists for self-evaluation
- Health stories written by teachers or others

● Guided reading, viewing or listening, followed by discussions

Teachers and health workers could, for instance, be asked to read a chapter of *Children for Health* every month and then meet for an afternoon to ask questions on it and discuss activities which could be done based on it. The same technique could be applied following a series of radio programmes. Tests could be set and a certificate awarded to those who had performed satisfactorily in them.

● Self-help seminars at school or outside it

We do not always need experts from outside. We also learn from sharing our ideas and experience. 'Health study groups' can be formed. Such groups have proved successful in primary school improvement projects in both Indonesia and India, though they have not yet been applied to health promotion. Groups appoint their own officers and organize their own programme of sharing experience. One way of raising incentives for such groups is to organize them partly in school time and partly in participants' own time. If, for instance, the group meets once a month for two hours it might be agreed that teachers could leave their classes one hour early.

QUESTIONS FOR EVERYONE

Approaches to teacher education

- Do we plan effectively?
- Do policy makers and programme planners have a wide enough view of teacher education?
- Or do they merely think of it as short courses for teachers?

At college level

- Is health being effectively taught at college level?
- Are colleges being encouraged to become health promoting?
- If not, how could this process be launched?
- Are colleges being linked to groups of schools in health-promotion programmes?
- Could they be?

When courses are organized

- Do we involve the right people, including children?
- Do we always set effective objectives for our courses and attempt to measure them?
- Do we plan them carefully with a realistic course programme?
- Do we allow plenty of time for discussion and practical work?

Alternatives to courses?

Do we plan and implement other effective ways of in-service education such as:

- Visits between schools?
- Help on the job?
- Planning and writing groups?
- Guided reading?
- Self-help seminars?

IDEAS FOR

 ## POLICY MAKERS

● Evaluation is necessary for all programmes.
● It needs to take place from the time a programme starts, and to focus not only on outcomes but also on whether a programme is being organized efficiently.
● It is difficult to measuring the effect of a school health programme by studying the statistics of disease; we need rather to measure the effect of a programme on health knowledge, health attitudes and health practice as well as on the acquisition of life skills.
● Good health programmes can affect the quality of both learning and life in schools; evaluation should look beyond health results.

 ## PROGRAMME DESIGNERS

● Evaluation needs to be built into programme design from the start.
● Objectives and baseline information are both necessary, so that we have something to compare.
● Checklists such as the ones included in this chapter are valuable and need to be made available to schools and projects. They are also useful when comparing schools.

 ## LOCAL PLANNERS, MANAGERS AND TRAINERS

● Everyone involved in a school health programme needs to be given training in simple evaluation. The techniques are *not* difficult. What is most important is to ask the right questions.
● One of the most important findings of a health education evaluation is whether those taking part in the programme want to continue doing it.

 ## SCHOOL AND COMMUNITY

● 'Insiders' – the heads, the teachers, the parents and the children are even more important to evaluation than outsiders such as project workers and supervisors. Everyone needs to ask questions at every stage of the programme so that it can be better organized and have a better effect on the health of children and their families.

Making a Difference: monitoring and evaluation

Part 1: The *Whys* and *Hows* of evaluation

> • What do we mean by 'evaluation ' and when do we do it? • Ways of collecting evidence ▪ Keeping diaries and records ▪ Questions and discussions ▪ Testing ▪ Observation • Evaluating changes in attitudes • Evaluating the success of the programme as a whole • Who evaluates? ▪ Why 'insiders', such as teachers, children and parents, are just as important as 'outsiders' such as inspectors.

Some people use the word **monitoring** to describe what we do when we observe a programme and collect information about it, and **evaluation** to describe the judgements people make when they have collected it. In fact, there are many overlaps in meaning between the two words. In this chapter we only use one word, *evaluation*.

The word evaluation sometimes frightens people. There is nothing unusual or difficult about it. We do it all the time. Whenever we do something in our lives we ask ourselves questions and make decisions:

• at the **beginning** of an activity
  e.g. why do I need to plant this crop, when and how?

• **during** an activity
  e.g. am I planting, tending and harvesting the crop efficiently?

• **at the end** of an activity
  e.g. was the crop as good as I expected it to be?
  did it make a difference to my life?
  was it worth the time, money or effort I put into growing it?
  how can I produce better crops next year?

Evaluating health promotion is a bit more difficult than this but it is still absolutely necessary and it still requires the same three stages. When we are **planning** and setting up the programme; while we are **doing** it; and when we have done it (or done part of it and are trying to find what the **outcomes** are).

Two key questions: at every stage
- Have we done it effectively? (Could we do it better, or do it better next time?)
- What difference have we made? (In what way and to whom?)

Changes we are looking for

We look for changes in three areas:

Knowledge and learning skills
Do people know more? Do they understand better? Do they know ways of finding out more? Do they know how to listen to others and communicate with them?

Practice
Are they doing new things? Are they doing them better? Are they doing them regularly? What has changed?

Attitudes
Have their attitudes changed towards themselves, towards others and towards their environment?

How can we find out whether changes are taking place?

In order to find out whether changes are taking place we need to be sure *what* changes we are hoping to achieve; in other words what we want our children, teachers and community to know, do and feel as a result of the new programme. These are the **objectives** of our programme. Objectives are essential. They need to be *clear* and *possible to measure* (though some of the most important outcomes, changes in attitudes and life skills may not be easy to measure precisely). Some of these objectives will relate to the **outcomes** of the programme. Yet other objectives will be about the **organization** of the programme.

Once we have found out how far we are meeting objectives we can then take decisions about what action to take. Evaluation provides information on which to make decisions.

Remember: evaluation which does not lead to action is a waste of time.

There are seven ways we can find out whether our programme is moving in the right direction, and whether we are meeting our objectives:

1. By keeping diaries and records

Both *teachers and pupils* could keep health diaries. The school health committee could produce a wall newspaper. The health club could keep a record of its meetings. After a time it will be possible to find out what has been done and to follow up some of the activities.

People from outside the school could visit regularly and keep records: the local health workers; the chair of the parents' committee; a tutor from a neighbouring teachers' college. A group of parents could be elected as health visitors and could come round every few months and describe what they see.

We see you are growing more green leafy vegetables.

2. By talking and discussing with people

Much of this activity is done informally as the programme develops, but sometimes we need to plan special occasions when we look for answers. We can do this by talking individually to children, parents, and teachers (using a list of questions and recording answers). Or we can plan discussion groups (sometimes called focus groups) where the group discusses the health programme and the organizer moves the discussion towards certain important issues and records the result. In every case it is important to ask questions which bring out real opinions rather than answers which the people you are questioning think you want.

3. By testing knowledge and skills

As we stressed in Chapter 3, correct knowledge is essential in health education. Wrong knowledge in other subjects can result in losing marks in examinations. Wrong knowledge in health can result in losing our lives. It is quite easy to find out whether children know health facts after the end of a lesson or at the end of a term, but this does not necessarily tell us whether they have learned anything new. If we can find out what children know to start with it also helps us plan our teaching better.

Give children a simple test on health content (especially that contained in *Children for Health*) before they have undertaken a topic, after you have finished it, and at the end of term (to see if they have remembered it). Use exactly the same questions every time.

Tests can use different types of questions. Here are three examples. The first, on malaria, uses multiple-choice questions. The second, on breastfeeding, uses true/false statements. The third, on child growth and development, asks pupils to 'fill in the blanks'. In each case the questions are carefully written so that they include a number of wrong beliefs and practices which are often held in communities. We must make sure that the children have 'lost' these beliefs.

Example (1) Malaria

Only one statement in each section is correct. The others are not. Mark the right statement.

a. The insects spread the disease throughout the day and night.

b. The insects spread the disease mostly in the evening and in the early part of the night.

c. The insects spread the disease all through the night including the hours before dawn.*

a. The insects which cause malaria breed mostly in flowing rivers and big lakes.

b. They breed mostly in small amounts of water which does not move (stagnant water).*

c. They breed mostly on dry rubbish dumps and in dirty smelly places.

a. A child with malaria should not be given too much to drink.

b. An ORS solution (containing water, sugar and salts) is the best drink for children with fever. *

c. Children with fever should be given plenty to drink but not ORS (that is for diarrhoea).

a. A child with fever must be kept cool (not cold) to prevent the temperature from rising .*

b. A child with fever must be wrapped up to help produce sweating and bring down the temperature.

c. A child with fever must be kept inside the house in a dark room to protect against cool breezes and sunlight.

Example (2) Breastfeeding

Some of the following statements are true and some are false. Tick the ones you think are true.

• Breast milk can supply all the fluid needs of a baby for the first six months. There is no need to give extra water, even in very hot climates. ✔

• It is best to start breastfeeding two days after birth when the mother is stronger. ✗

• The thicker yellowish milk - colostrum, produced in the first few days after birth is not good for a baby. ✗

• Do not stop breastfeeding when the baby is unwell. The baby needs the fluid and the nourishment. ✔

Example (3) child growth and development

Fill in the blanks:

- Children from birth to three years need to be weighed every (_____) (*month*). If there is no weight gain after (_____) (*two*) months something is wrong.
- A child under three years needs food (_____ or _____) (*five or six*) times a day because it needs a great deal of energy and because its (_____) (*stomach*) is very small.
- Children need food which is rich in Vitamin A. Many children go (_____) (*blind*) every year because they do not have enough vitamin A in their bodies. Vitamin A is found in (_____) (*green*) coloured vegetable leaves and (_____) (*orange*) coloured fruits and vegetables like (_____) (*local names*).

Other ways of testing knowledge and skills in pupils

- Give them simple problems and ask them to tell you what they would do in the following examples:
- You have a baby with diarrhoea at home
i. How would you treat the baby?
ii. How will you make sure that other people in the house are not infected?
- Your younger sister puts her fingers into the cooking pot and they are badly burned. What should you do immediately?
- Your friend falls from a tree. He does not get up but he is crying and his arm is bleeding. What should you do?
- You discover that a child in your house has a very high fever. What should you do?
- Ask them to show you something they have learnt: e.g. making a sling for first aid, or making an arm-circumference measure.

4. By observation

By looking at the buildings and surroundings

Has the health programme made an impact on the appearance of the school? Is it brighter, tidier, cleaner? (Or just the same?)

By looking at regular practices around the school.

Are there any changes in sanitation and water practices? (Or none?) Have food hygiene and food production improved? (Or not?) Has provision for safety and first aid been improved? (Or is it unaffected?) Are teachers and children beginning regularly to carry out simple preventive health actions (see Chapter 6) as part of school routine?

By observing changes in the way children act and behave

In other words we need to find out from children, and also from teachers, whether they are *doing* more to keep themselves healthy and to promote health in others, and whether their *attitudes* have changed. We need to find out four main types of things.

● Have they *made or done* anything for the new health programme, e.g. written a song, made a poster, or made a toy; read a story to a younger child; taken part in a health march? If so, ask them to show everyone what they have made and to tell you about it. How interested and enthusiastic do they sound? Have they (with their friends) had any new ideas and acted on them?

● See whether their *health behaviour has changed* at school. Are they, for instance, cleaner, tidier, and more helpful to younger children? Are they more aware of the need to help and comfort others who have problems,

We made this for her. It makes her laugh

and more interested in health activities (or has the programme made little change to them)?

● Find out whether they have *taken ideas home*. Ask them to tell you what they have done and question them closely to see whether they can clearly describe to you any actions they have taken. Ask them whether their own behaviour has changed at home and if so in what way. If possible, also ask parents or older brothers and sisters what they have said or done.

● Find out from *school heads* and *health workers* what their views are about what the children have achieved. Many people who invest money in school health programmes like to ask for *proof* that these programmes have had an effect on the health statistics of communities. This is very difficult without an expensive research programme. However, the health workers and school heads may be able to say 'we *think* there is less scabies this year as a result of the school programme', or 'we *think* that the fall in road accidents is due to the school campaign'. Such information is very valuable.

'It says here feed in the data to your computer and conduct a multiple regression analysis.'

By observing changes in teachers and the community

Note whether teachers, parents and members of school health committees seem to have changed the way that they behave, e.g. by showing more interest in health and safety matters or by taking action recommended by the school, such as providing more or different food for children to bring from home to school.

5. By finding out whether attitudes have changed

Since the most important aim of health promotion in schools is to help children develop positive attitudes towards health which will stay with them after they have left school, all evaluation programmes would like us to measure attitudes. This is not easy. Tests and questionnaires exist but are of little help. Four ways of measuring are useful:

Setting up 'indicators' based on what children do, and comparing results over a certain time.

We could look at these indicators at regular times (perhaps every three months) as they relate to children in a school or project. Provided there are enough children and the observing and recording is fairly done, well-chosen indicators should tell us a great deal about changes in attitude. The table below lists some of the indicators we could use.

- Regular attendance at school. Days off sick or for some other reason.

- Evidence of attendance in any health activity, e.g. club, project, committee.

- Evidence of helping young children at school or home; new activities with them.

- Involvement in keeping the school and home environment clean.

- Evidence of showing spontaneous concern for the environment.

- Evidence of active and responsible action towards the health and safety of others.

- Change in hygiene habits or keeping up new habits (such as washing hands)

- Changes in eating habits, such as always eating before going off to school or eating more fruit.

- Special interest and involvement in any new health priority identified by the school. Has the child done something new or special, such as making a poster or taking part in a play?

- Evidence of children becoming more creative and questioning in their school work.

- General impression of a child's interest and liveliness in class.

Asking independent observers to comment on whether schools and children have changed. The observers could visit the schools from time to time. Here are some of the things they could ask.

- Is the school clean and attractive? Do the children play a role in it? Do they seem proud of it?
- Are any *new* hygiene or safety improvements visible?
- Can teachers and children identify priority health needs and say what they hope will improve. . . and how this might take place?
- What evidence is there of *recent* health activities . . .things that children have made up, done or written about? Do these activities show signs of thought and initiative, or are they mostly confined to songs and slogans copied from somewhere else or repeated year in and year out, thus made up *for* the school and not *by* the school?
- What *new* evidence is there of children taking ideas to others? Can they tell you about it?

Ask children to make up or respond to role-playing situations. Here are some examples:

- Your cousin who comes to stay is disabled and has to walk on crutches. You and your friends want to play football. (What can you do?)
- A new child of eighteen months has come into the family. Her parents have died. She is rather small and doesn't seem to talk or play. She just sits and sometimes cries. (What do you do?)
- There are cases of cholera reported in your town. Your auntie, who is a very strict lady, tells you that you will be quite safe if you keep away from anyone who might be infected and wash your vegetables well. (What can you do and tell her?)
- You learn your uncle has AIDS. Your family does not want you to see him. (What can you do?)

Ask teachers whether the programme has led to any changes in the way they think about health and about children's role in health promotion.

Their answers may indicate that they have changed their views about what children can do or that they have gained greater respect for them. The answers may even show us that the teachers themselves are beginning to think in a different way about health practices, about the role of girls and boys in health promotion, or even about the way the teachers themselves prepare and teach their classes. These would be powerful arguments in favour of retaining or extending the programme.

6. By finding out whether the programme has had any effect on teaching and learning practices in other subjects

Once teachers and children have used certain ways of learning in health topics it is possible that they will try them out in lessons in other subjects. In Chapter 2 we emphasized the importance of developing life skills, and in Chapter 3 we discussed ways of learning which developed active thinking in children and which linked home with school, and learning with action. So when we evaluate the way health education is taught and learnt we need to go a little further, asking questions such as:

- In what other subjects do you use these methods?
- Do you use the Child-to-Child approach in other subjects. If so which ones?
- Can learning in other subjects be applied straight away in the home? How?
- Do you encourage it?
- In addition to *Health across the curriculum* what other themes can be spread in the same way? Have you tried to spread them?

---

7. By finding out whether the programme has made any difference to the life of the school as a whole

Many people using new health programmes report that they have changed the life of schools and sometimes of communities as well, in ways which are not directly related to changes in health. Some of these could be positive and some negative.

Nearly always heads and organizers will have to deal with both kinds of comments and will have to assess which are the most frequent and most important. Probably the most significant question to ask to find out people's overall impression of the programme is, '*Do you want the school to carry on with the programme. . . if so, why? If not why not?*'

How can we find out whether the organization and management of a project are effective?

As we pointed out in Chapter 7 we need to evaluate our planning as well as the results we have achieved. All the different tasks on pages 110-114 need to be the subject of evaluation questions right from the start of the programme. Thus *before any action has even started in schools* we need to be asking questions such as:

> • Have the right people been consulted? National officials? Local leaders and administrators?
>
> • Do they understand and approve the purpose of the project?
>
> • Have both education and health workers been involved from the beginning?
>
> • Do all those who have to take action know and understand the project and its purpose?
>
> • Have needs been identified carefully and realistic priorities chosen?
>
> • Have present practices and beliefs been surveyed?
>
> • Has an effective plan of action been made?
>
> • Are the objectives and tasks realistic?
>
> • Have those who will be carrying out the plan had a part in making it, so that they feel that they 'own' it in some way?
>
> • Are there sufficient resources (people, materials, money) to enable the plan to work?
>
> • Is there sufficient resource material? Can it be easily understood and used? Is it relevant and medically correct?

Unless such evaluation takes place at the beginning there is a distinct chance that a programme may be setting off in the wrong direction. The longer it travels along the wrong road the more difficult it is to turn back.

The evaluation then needs to continue through every stage, e.g. **when schools are identified**.

> • Have schools and, or, classes taking part in the project been well identified?
>
> • Have plans been made to give the right kind of training to those who need it?
>
> • Are the objectives for this training clear, appropriate and workable?

When training takes place

> • Was it effectively organized? How could it have been improved?
>
> • Did it meet its objectives
>
> • Were effective plans made for follow up and further training activities?

> • Are there working groups or committees responsible for the management of the programme at both project level and school level?
>
> • Have they a clear plan and do they each understand their part in making it work?
>
> • Does effective evaluation of activities form an important part of the plan so that everyone knows what to look for and how to suggest changes where necessary?
>
> • Is the purpose of the project understood by all teachers and children in the school, and can they see how it will help them?

... and so on at every stage as the programme develops and changes.

Who evaluates?

Many people believe that monitoring and evaluation is done by outsiders who visit programmes and decide how well they are running and how good they are. There is a place for outside evaluation, but the most important evaluation of any programme comes from those who plan it, manage it and work it. In this case that means local planners and managers in health and education, together with the heads, the teachers, the parents and even the children themselves. If everyone knows what the programme is trying to achieve, and everyone knows the right questions to ask to find out whether it is achieving it, then the programme can be monitored and evaluated at all three stages mentioned at the beginning of this chapter. At the end of this chapter we include a checklist. Such a list can be used by both 'insiders' and 'outsiders' at every stage in the programme to see how far schools are becoming health promoting.

The most important questions

Good monitoring and evaluation give us **evidence** on which to make up our minds about how far a programme has met its objectives and how well it has been managed. The more we get and the better we get, the easier it will be for us to improve the programme. In order to make wise decisions two things are essential.
First: we need to know what the objectives are, so that we can see how far our programme has reached them.
Second: we need to know which are the most important questions to ask.

Here are eight of the most essential ones.

1. As a result of the programme have the children (and the teachers) learnt more about health?

2. Has it changed the way they think and act?

3. Has it contributed to the way that children learn and apply what they learn?

4. Has it improved the school as a whole in any way?

5. Has it, in any way, helped to link the school closer with the community?

6. Has it brought the head and the teachers closer to the community health workers?

7. Has it been planned and organized efficiently and with the participation of all those who are taking part in it?

8. Has it been worth the effort spent on it?

If the answer to most of these questions is 'yes', then the programme was almost certainly worthwhile. If the answers are generally 'no' then there is a lot of thinking to be done.

QUESTIONS FOR EVERYONE

The definition of evaluation

• How can we persuade people, including ourselves, that evaluation is necessary right from the beginning of very programme, and that it is there to help us do things better, rather than to point out what we have done wrong?

• How can we persuade people not to be frightened of evaluation?

Who evaluates?

• How can we persuade everybody who is working on the project that they are evaluators?

• How can we persuade them to evaluate themselves and what they are doing rather than wait for others to come from outside and evaluate them?

• What simple training is necessary on evaluation and for whom?

How and when can we evaluate?

• How can we ensure that simple baseline data is collected before a programme starts, so as to give us something to compare with as the programme develops?

• How can we ensure that objectives are set and that all those involved in a project, including the teachers and, where relevant, the children know what the objectives are?

• How can we make a simple and workable plan for evaluating our own programmes?

• Who would be involved in seeing that this plan is followed through?

The tools of evaluation

• What simple materials may be available or may need to be produced to help us evaluate?

• How far can the checklist in Part 2 be used and adapted?

Acting on evaluation

• How can we make sure that any evaluation we have done leads to action?

Part 2: A checklist for a health-promoting school

Who this checklist is for

This checklist has two purposes:

- It can be used by people **outside** the school to assess how far schools are becoming 'health promoting' (possibly being used in 'healthy school' competitions).

- It can be used by people **inside** the school (such as heads, teachers and even groups of children) to check progress of schools in their attempts to become more 'health promoting'.

The headings in the checklist

There are six headings. Not all should be give the same weighting and a division into percentage points is suggested. Both headings and weighting are provisional and local programmes will certainly wish to review and reorganize them. It is also possible to use the checklist without marks and percentages and many schools and programmes may wish to do this.

Headings:

1. **School:** the place (16 points)

2. **School:** the people (20 points)

3. **School:** the health education programme (36 points)

   Includes: The content

   The methodology and approaches used

   Extension into school, home and community

   Monitoring and evaluation

4. **Keeping in touch** (10 points)

   Includes: Communication with other agencies

   Training

5. **Health services in and for the school** (8 Points)

6. **General impressions** (including the happiness and general well-being of the school) (10 points)

THE CHECKLIST

1 School: the place

1.1 Where learning takes place (4 points)

This may vary from a good permanent building to something less permanent or even no building at all.

We need to ask:

▪ Is the learning place clean and safe to study in, well cared for, hygienic?

Score highest marks where the greatest effort has been made.

Score lowest marks where the learning place is dirty, unhygienic and shows no evidence of effort or self-respect.

COMMENT ....

1.2 The surroundings (1): appearance (4 points)

We need to ask:

▪ Are the surroundings as clean, well maintained, welcoming and as attractive as possible?

Score highest marks where greatest effort has been made. Score lowest marks where virtually no interest or effort is evident.

COMMENT ....

1.3 The surroundings (2): safety and freedom from pests (4 points)

We need to ask:

▪ Are the surroundings as safe as possible (e.g. road crossings; electrical hazards, grass cut [snakes]; mosquito breeding places eliminated)?

Score highest marks where real care is evident.

Score lowest marks where no care is shown and there are visible safety hazards which have been ignored.

COMMENT ....

1.4 The surroundings (3): sanitation and water hygiene (4 points)

We need to ask:

▪ Are there latrines and if so are they clean?

If there are no latrines are there rules and practices which are effective and observed?

Is the best possible water supply available for the school (given local circumstances)?

Are hand-washing facilities provided?

Score highest marks where greatest effort has been made.

Score lowest marks where there is virtually no evidence of good hygiene and sanitation.

Note: However, since latrines are so important for hygiene, only schools with latrines can score 3 or 4 marks.

COMMENT ....

2 School: the people

2.1 The pupils (1): appearance and activity (4 points)

We need to ask:

Are the pupils clean and do they demonstrate good hygiene practices and habits?

Do older children refrain from habits which will damage their health, e.g. smoking?

Score highest marks where pupils clearly take pride in their appearance and show evidence of regularly following hygiene and safety rules.

Score lowest marks where pupils are dirty and act unhygienically or carelessly.

Note: Be very careful not to reward children who are richer, and who may have newer or more expensive clothes, for example, above others who are less fortunate. What is important is the care children take to keep clean and hygienic.

COMMENT ....

2.2 The pupils (2): interest and attitude (4 points)

We need to ask:

Are the pupils evidently interested in making their school health promoting?

Do they try to make other children (especially those younger than themselves) clean and health/safety conscious?

Do they try to promote good health habits in others (especially children of their own age)?

Score highest marks where there is obvious enthusiasm, activity and pride by the pupils.

Score lowest marks where no activity takes place and children are unaware that they have any part to play.

COMMENT ....

2.3 The teachers (4 points)

We need to ask:

▪ Do teachers understand the new ideas, are they committed to them and are they themselves setting good health and safety examples?

Score highest marks for active and committed teachers, and particularly for those who do set good health examples.

Score lowest marks for those who show no interest and compound this by demonstrating unhealthy practices to their pupils.

COMMENT ....

2.4 The administrators (4 points)

We need to ask:

▪ Are heads, inspectors and local health workers aware of the goals of a 'healthy school' movement?

▪ Do they understand and support them and are they prepared to take action rather than give merely lip-service to them?

Score highest marks where there is both understanding and commitment and where administrators are willing to give resources (particularly time) to health promotion in their schools.

Score lowest marks where there is little or no commitment.

COMMENT ....

2.5 The community (4 points)

We need to ask:

▪ Does the community show interest and involvement in the health activities in the school?

▪ Does the community actively cooperate in making its school a more healthy place and its children more healthy individuals?

Score highest marks where evidence of real cooperation is evident, with parents clearly supporting the school and encouraging their children.

Score lowest marks where there is no evidence of interest, or even outright distrust, between community and school.

COMMENT ....

3 School: the health education programme

3.1 The content of the programme (6 points)

We need to ask:

- Is the content *relevant* to the health needs of the learners?
- Is the content *related* to the age and interests of the children?
- Is the content *realistic*, given the human and material resources available?

Score highest marks for interesting and well-chosen content.

Score lowest marks for content which is unrelated to needs, unchallenging and dull.

COMMENT ....

3.2 How the content is used (6 points)

We need to ask:

- Is the content effectively followed and taught?
- Is the time available managed adequately?
- Are messages reinforced, where possible, across the curriculum?
- Is there evidence of imagination and flexibility to meet changing needs and interests?

Score highest marks for effective learning and teaching which shows that teachers and children really understand the objectives and spirit as well as the letter of the programme.

Score lowest marks for a programme which is planned but not followed. A programme which is followed but without real understanding cannot gain more than half marks.

COMMENT ....

3.3 Methods and approaches (1): active or passive? (4 points)

We need to ask:

- Are effective and challenging methods and materials being used?
- Do they involve children not only in activity but in active learning and thinking?
- Do they make learning enjoyable and interesting?
- Do they involve all the children and not just some of them?

Score highest marks for lively and interesting methods which help develop children's understanding. Score lowest marks for dull, rote methods.

COMMENT ....

3.4 Methods and approaches (2): inward or outward-looking? (4 points)

We need to ask:

Do methods and learning materials link learning in the classroom with life skills at home?

When health topics are reinforced across the curriculum, do the methods used help strengthen learning and understanding in the subjects in which they are used?

Score highest marks for methods which 'lead out' children towards new learning in other subjects and at home.

Score lowest marks for 'learn and test' methods which are not related to real life.

COMMENT ....

3.5 Extension into school and community (6 points)

We need to ask:

Does the programme effectively aim to complement classroom teaching with regular activity around the school?

Is learning in school transferred into the community though joint school/community activities, or less formally through Child-to-Child activities?

Are children involved in planning community activities rather than merely carrying out a programme entirely designed by adults?

When activities are taken to communities, are culturally acceptable approaches used?

Score highest marks for programmes which are frequent, effective and culturally acceptable.

Score lowest marks when no attempts have been made. Programmes which show a lack of sensitivity or which use children as 'loudspeakers' do not gain high marks.

COMMENT ....

3.6 Monitoring progress of programmes (4 points)

We need to ask:

Is the day-to-day progress of the health programme being monitored?

Are all participants involved (e.g. organizers, teachers and pupils) in trying to find out how to 'do it better' (e.g. through keeping records, periodic discussions at staff meetings and maintaining a working health committee)?

Is action taken on feedback?

Score highest marks where all know the purpose of monitoring the programme and are involved in it.

Score lowest marks when nobody feels involved and all are waiting for someone else to tell them before they do anything.

COMMENT ....

3.7 Evaluating the impact of the programme (6 points)

We need to ask:

 Are effective attempts being made to find out the impact of the programme through continuous assessment of pupils?

 ... through periodic tests of knowledge and skills?

 ... through assessing the impact of health action on children and their families?

Score highest marks when there is an effective programme and when all those involved are interested in finding out the impact they have made.

Score lowest marks when no one knows or cares whether any changes have taken place in knowledge, attitudes or practice.

COMMENT ....

4 Information and communication

4.1 Channels of communication (4 points)

We need to ask:

 Are there effective channels of communication between education and health workers and with other sectors in the community?

 Are information and materials (e.g. publications and broadcasts) used and shared?

 Does the school effectively communicate with the leaders of its community?

 Is there an effective communication and understanding between the school at local level and programmes at central level?

Score highest marks when there is real sharing of ideas and understanding of how better communication can help to make schools better agents of health promotion.

Score lowest marks where there is virtually no communication or understanding.

COMMENT ....

4.2 Training (including informal sharing of knowledge and practice) (6 points)

We need to ask:

☐ Are teachers and administrators given as much training as is possible given resources available?

☐ Does the training unite the knowledge and skills of both the education and health sectors?

☐ Is it relevant and effective? Is it ongoing?

☐ Are those with knowledge and experience regularly used to help others implement the new ideas?

Score highest marks where training is both relevant and cost-effective, and where everyone involved in the programme sees it as a responsibility to communicate what he or she knows or is doing to others.

Score lowest marks where no training is taking place and no attempts are being made to share experience.

COMMENT ....

5 Health services

5.1 Health services provided *for* the school (4 points)

We need to ask:

☐ Are health services, to the best of their ability:
Helping schools prevent disease and ill health occurring, e.g. through advice about hygiene and nutrition and actions such as immunization.
Helping them to identify problems early so than action can be taken early, e.g. through screening children, and teaching schools how to recognize danger signs.
Giving support and advice to schools in dealing with long-term health problems, e.g. children with home difficulties and emotional problems, or children with disabilities or other long term conditions.

Note: We need carefully to assess resources here and not expect the impossible. Clearly rural areas in poorer countries and communities will be able to provide much less than urban areas in richer communities.

Score highest marks where the health sector puts a high priority on helping schools, where it does so in a cost-effective way (e.g. by targeting areas of need) and where it tries to work in partnership with the school – advising them on how they can provide services themselves and offering them support when they need it.

Score lowest marks where the health services have little or no involvement in the school health programme.

COMMENT ....

5.2 Health services provided *by* and *from* the school (4 points)

We need to ask:

▧ Does the school (head/teachers/children/community) do all in its power to take action to provide health services at all three levels mentioned in Chapter 7?

- Through developing a school which seeks to *prevent* ill health?

- Through identification of children with health problems (e.g. malnutrition, emotional difficulties or eyesight deficiencies)?

- Through treatment of those who are sick and unhappy (e.g. first aid, or support and understanding when children suffer unhappiness at home)?

- Through managing long-term conditions (e.g. children with disabilities)?

- Through referral of those who need treatment (e.g. arranging for them to be taken to health centres or clinics)?

Score highest marks for schools which show the greatest degree of understanding, commitment and action; where teachers, children and parents realize how much they can do on their own, and where they must try to seek help.

Score lowest marks for schools which lack the knowledge or will to help those who are sick or unhappy. Low marks must also to be given to schools where sick children are identified but where no one takes action or responsibility until medical help is available.

COMMENT ....

6 General impression

**The school as a healthy environment for learning and living
(10 points)**

Mark the school from 1-10 on your general impression of how far it
is a healthy place, in all senses of the word – mental and social as
well as physical. Pay particular attention to:

- whether the school is a true community with everyone working
towards certain goals;

- whether the children in it care about making their communities
better places;

- whether the school raises the self-esteem of children and teachers;

- whether they are proud of it and feel safe and happy in it;

- whether children are respected and their rights upheld;

- whether all children feel they have equal chances.

*Note: Although this section is difficult to score, such overall
impressions are important. It is possible to have a school which is
very clean and hygienic but where children are not valued.
Alternatively, a school might score low in many aspects of this
checklist but remain one in which children are happy and have their
self-esteem raised. This section helps to record these positive and
negative impressions.*

COMMENT ....

CHAPTER 10

Resources and How to Use Them

• Financial resources; what is needed and where help may be sought
• How to convince people to invest their time in school health promotion • Human resources at national and local level; how to use them • Material resources, especially written ones, and where to obtain them

If we are to introduce comprehensive health promotion into our schools we will need the resources to do it. Resources include:

Money

For most people the word resources means money. Comprehensive school health education will require money for training and for resource materials. The amounts needed are not great. If a country, a local project or a school wishes to start a reasonable programme it is likely that they will find the support to do so. There is much concern about health in schools. Therefore, many international and national agencies and NGOs, and even private businesses and individuals, may be prepared to help programmes get started. They only need to be convinced that such projects will be effective in improving the health of children and communities.

The following large agencies have supported programmes which include new approaches to school health:
UNICEF
ODA (British Aid)
Danida (Danish Aid)
Cida (Canadian Aid)
Save the Children Fund, UK
Rada Barnan (SCF Sweden)
AMREF (East Africa)
Comic Relief (Africa)
CRY (Child Relief and You), India
The Aga Khan Foundation
The Bernard Van Leer Foundation
PLAN International
together with a number of agencies and religious bodies. Often embassies from European or North American countries are able to make small grants without referring to their national aid agencies.

This is not to say that money will not be needed to meet some needs identified by the programme. In many cases the causes of poor health are closely linked to community needs such as poor water supply and sanitation, lack of land and food, environmental pollution and poor housing, all of which require a great deal of money to put right. But lack of funds or poor health conditions should never prevent a programme from starting. There is always something that schools can do and one of the most important things is to get children and adults talking about their health needs and making them known clearly and loudly to those who maybe able to help them.

COMPREHENSIVE SCHOOL HEALTH PROMOTION – SOME ARGUMENTS WORTH USING

- 50% of the world's population are children. We owe it to them to provide effective health education NOW.
- Healthy teachers find teaching easier and teach better. They act as an example to children and help to provide a positive go-ahead atmosphere in the school.
- Healthy children do better at school.
- Healthy schools (especially those where children learn life skills through health education) get better academic results.
- Currently many children enter school with disadvantages because their health has suffered as a result of conditions during pregnancy and during early childhood. We need to educate future mothers and fathers, where we can reach them – at SCHOOL.
- Children *in* school are frequently unhealthy and unhappy. This affects their learning as well as their being. Good health promotion in school can help these children especially during their adolescence, and save them from wasting their lives and their schools' time and effort.
- Comprehensive school health promotion teaches children to act responsibly in looking after their own health. We need this responsible thought and action more today than ever before.
- Working TOGETHER we can improve our health and the health of our communities and our environment.
- Health promotion is thus an investment in development.

Time

What is more difficult to find than money is time. Making schools and communities healthier takes time: time to plan, time to convince people, time to teach and learn new things.

In order for people to spend time they must really be convinced that the new ideas are worthwhile. This book is filled with ideas and experience which, if used, can make comprehensive school health programmes both interesting and effective. Unless these ideas are spread among many people and *unless people are able to say these are* **our** ideas, **we** talked about them, **we** developed them, **we** explained them to others and **we** saw them working, *then they will never catch on.* Spreading the information about the programme, getting people to talk about it also takes time, but it is time very well spent.

Human resources (people) at national level

The table below suggests some of the people at national level who may be able to help when comprehensive school health-promotion programmes are being organized. It is drawn from experience in organizing health action programmes involving 'children for health'.

Politicians

May be interested in the idea. *Better Health for our Schools*, and *Children for Health* are strong statements. But be careful. Politicians often want ideas to spread very quickly and reach out to all citizens, so explain that the movement must grow slowly.

Policy makers and planners in health and education

Potential organizers of programmes at national level are also necessary to provide support and 'blessing' for local programmes. Let us hope that they fully understand the concept of comprehensive school health promotion and that different sectors all have the same view and cooperate one with another.

University staff

Always interested in new approaches and may agree to 'write up' the programme or to involve their students in describing or evaluating local activities in schools. University paediatricians may well cooperate in 'Training of trainers' courses.

Teachers' associations

These often support school-based action and have proved interested in the idea of health-promoting schools. There is similar support from their international body, Education International.

Organizers of national voluntary bodies (NGOs)

Scouts, guides and other youth groups are always interested in health action programmes involving children. They fit in well with the 'badge system'. Other bodies which concentrate on specific areas of health such as clean water, hygiene and sanitation, and environmental protection, can easily see the value of health-promoting schools which stress these things.

Radio and television programmes

Can strongly promote the ideas once good 'Health Action' programmes have started in schools and can be shown to be interesting and exciting. Many programmes also exist in which children from schools promote health ideas though activities such as songs and plays. Some of these are presented by children themselves. A book and tape *We Are On The Radio* has been produced by the Child-to-Child Trust to help those who plan such programmes.

Musicians, film and sports personalities

May be persuaded to give public support to programmes and many have done so. Be careful that those who give support set a good health example themselves.

People who can help at local level

Here the list is even longer. It includes:

Hospital doctors (usually paediatricians)
These are often prepared to help on training courses. Because they have to communicate with families they are often very good with teachers.

Retired education and health workers
These may often agree to serve on school health committees or to become patrons of children's health clubs.

Local business people
They can help with donations of materials and sometimes money for school activities. Be sure to give them the publicity they deserve for the help they have given.

Local story tellers and musicians
They can help promote health messages for the school and, better still, work with children to show them how *they* can spread their ideas to others.

Religious leaders
They will be particularly interested in the way health promotion encourages children to help others, and in the new definitions of health as good social behaviour as well as good physical health.

Youth workers
They will be very eager to cooperate in out-of-school activities, particularly with those which involve children who are not in school alongside school children.

Women's groups
They will welcome the way the programmes stress that boys and girls have equal responsibilities for health. The content of the health messages which stress the importance of child development and nutrition for women and girls will also help them.

Our resources

Material resources for schools

Resources from shops and businesses

Sometimes businesses may donate goods such as seeds, soap, paper or building materials. More often they can be approached to give things which they cannot use themselves: e.g. off-cuts of wood, wire, cloth or paper for puppets or toy making, cardboard for posters and games, old newspapers and magazines for pictures to cut out.

Resources from the environment

These include grass, branches and fibre to make refuse bins and brooms; clay for models and puppets; seeds and cuttings for gardens. . . and much more.

Resources from the children

Remember that children themselves are excellent resources for health, especially for learning about our bodies and learning about growth and development. Why show something on a poster if you can show it on a child!

Written resources

The following books are useful, relatively easy to obtain and not too expensive. If possible, programmes should buy them and make them available to programme planners and to schools.

Feel your rib cage here. Your lungs are inside it.

Children for Health

Available from UNICEF New York or TALC (see below).

We recommend that *Children for Health* be used alongside this book. It is in two parts. The first part (35 pages) shows all the ways in which children become partners in health promotion in schools and from schools. The second part (135 pages), includes all the prime messages and supporting information contained in *Facts for Life*, with two additional sections – Accidents and Nutrition. It thus expands greatly on the information contained in Appendix 1 of this book which only lists the prime messages. All facts are those which are currently agreed by the World Health Organization. Each of the twelve main sections is followed by a set of objectives for children's understanding and action, and suggestions on how schools should introduce the themes. The activities themselves are subdivided into activities which promote *understanding* and activities which promote *action*.

Eight other important resource books

1. *Resource Book, Part 2*, Child-to-Child Trust, London, 1994.
Contains activity sheets under eight sub-headings, including Disability, Child Growth and Development, and Children in Especially Difficult Circumstances, which deal with topics not available or not fully treated in *Children for Health*. Each activity sheet has both factual information and suggestions for methods.

2. Fuerstein M.T., *Partners in Evaluation*, Macmillan, London, 1986.
A simple guide to those evaluating programmes.

3. Gibbs and Mutunga, *Health into Mathematics*, Longman, Harlow, 1991. Contains many useful examples on health activities in mathematics classes for primary schools.

4. Savage, King F., and Burgess A., *Nutrition in Developing Countries*, ELBS with Oxford University Press, Oxford, 1992. Excellent, up-to-date information about all aspects of nutrition.

5. Werner D., *Where There is No Doctor*, Macmillan, London, 1992. Comprehensive yet readable medical information.

6. Werner D., *Disabled Village Children*, Hesperian Foundation, Palo Alto, 1987.

7. Werner and Bower, *Helping Health Workers Learn*, Hesperian Foundation, Palo Alto. Contains a wealth of material on methodology and the organization of in-service programmes. Very easy to read.

8. Young and Durston, *Primary Health Education*, Longman, Harlow, 1987. An excellent introduction to the teaching of health education in primary schools.

Health storybooks for children

A number of story books on health topics have been published by the Child-to-Child Trust and have been translated and adapted in many languages. English stories include *Child-to-Child Readers* (currently 15), published by Longman and available in book shops or through TALC (see below).

Visual aids

TALC also publish excellent slide-sets, especially useful for teaching about health-scale, as well a new Child-to-Child height-scale mentioned in Chapter 6.

Where to get publications

All books in English listed here are available from: Teaching-aids At Low Cost (TALC), PO Box 49, St Albans, Herts., AL1 4AX, United Kingdom.

Other useful addresses for other languages include:

Arab Resource Collective (ARC), PO Box 730, Nicosia, Cyprus
(A large selection of relevant books in Arabic, including translations of many of the above).

L'Enfant pour L'Enfant, Institut Santé et Developpement, 15 rue de l'Ecole de medecine, 75270 Paris, France
All-French material related to Child-to-Child approaches, including an excellent series of storybooks with detailed back-up notes.

Voluntary Health Association of India (VHAI), Tong Swasthya Bhavan, 40 Institutional Area, South of IIT, New Delhi, 110 016, India
Resource material including manuals, storybooks and games in English, Hindi and Indian regional languages.

Centre for Health Education and Nutrition Awareness (CHETNA), Lilavatiben Lalbhai's Bungalow, Civil Camp Road, Shahibang Ahmadebad, 380 004 Gujarat, India
Much resource material; also publishes *Children for Health* in Hindi and Gujarati. UNICEF regional and country offices.

The Middle East Regional Office (Jordan) and the Latin American Regional Office (Columbia) have produced Arabic and Spanish versions of *Children for Health*. The office in Iran has produced a version in Farsi.

WHO offices and publications

The Health Education and Health Promotion Unit, World Health Organization, CH-1211, Geneva 27, Switzerland (Fax 004122 7910746) is committed to the concept of comprehensive school health promotion and publishes much relevant material e.g.

The report *Promoting Health Through Schools* WHO/HPR/HEP/ 96.4, December 1996.

Life Skills Education for Children and Adolescents in Schools, 1993

Much useful material on AIDS and STD education, e.g. *Handbook for Planners*, WHO/GPA/TCO/PRV/94.6a, and the *1994 Teachers' Guide*, WHO/GPA/TCO/PRV/94.6b, 1994.

Regional offices, especially those in India (New Delhi) and the eastern Mediterranean (Alexandria), produce locally relevant publications.

APPENDIX: PRIORITY HEALTH THEMES SOME ESSENTIAL INFORMATION

This appendix contains essential health information on the six key health themes identified in Chapter 2. Each theme is divided into several topics. In ten cases the text of each topic has been taken directly from *Facts for Life* and *Children for Health* (which have the same wording for the ten health messages), and in a further two cases – *Accidents* and *Food for the family* – the text is based on *Children for Health*, as these two themes do not occur in the English version of *Facts for Life*. In all these twelve themes, supplementary information is available in *Children for Health*, together with objectives for children's understanding and action, and a great variety of activities which can be undertaken in class, around the school and in the community. Three topics – *Worms and parasites*, *Substance abuse*, and *Working with disabled children* – and a note on *micronutrients* are introduced in this book only.

One of the main aims of the theme *Growth* is for children to understand how their bodies work and in particular to understand how their bodies and their emotions change at puberty. Knowledge of these changes and of how sexual development takes place are a vital component of health education. At the end of this appendix we therefore include some notes about issues that need to be taught, learnt and, above all, discussed. But supplementary information is also needed. Good school textbooks in biology help to give such information as does our recommended book, *Primary Health Education* (see page 166 for details).

Contents of the Appendix

Theme 1 – Hygiene
Topics:
Personal and community hygiene
Diarrhoea
Worms and parasites

Theme 2 – Nutrition
Topics:
Breastfeeding
Food for the family
Note: Three micronutrients.

Theme 3 – Growth and development
Topics:
Child growth
Child development
Safe motherhood
[See also notes on coping with adolescence, on page 181.]

Theme 4 – Infectious diseases
Topics:
Malaria
Immunization
Coughs and colds

Theme 5 – Safety and safe lifestyles
Topics:
Accidents
Substance abuse
AIDS

Theme 6 – Working with disabled people

Note
Coping with adolescence: how our bodies and emotions change at puberty

Theme 1

Hygiene

Personal and community hygiene

More than half of all the illness and death among young children is caused by germs which get into the child's mouth via food and water. Thus knowledge about good hygiene is vital to children as individuals, as family members and as future parents. They can also be a powerful force in bringing to communities the importance of good hygiene practices and in adding their voice to those who demand more support for community services, such as clean water and latrines.

Prime messages

1. Illnesses can be prevented by washing hands with soap and water after contact with faeces and before handling food.

2. Illnesses can be prevented by using latrines.

3. Illnesses can be prevented by using clean water.

4. Illnesses can be prevented by boiling drinking water if it is not from a safe piped supply.

5. Raw food is often dangerous. It should be washed or cooked. Cooked food should be eaten straight away, not left to stand. Warmed-up food should be thoroughly reheated.

6. Illnesses can be prevented by keeping food clean.

7. Illnesses can be prevented by burning or burying household refuse.

See *Facts for Life* page 61 or *Children for Health* page 87 for supporting information.

Diarrhoea

Diarrhoea causes dehydration and malnutrition, and kills over three million children every year. Nearly all these deaths can be prevented. Older children have a key role both as family and as future parents, in understanding the dangers of dehydration and learning to take action to prevent it at home. They can recognize when dehydration is severe and needs medical help.

Prime messages

1. Diarrhoea can kill by draining too much liquid from the body, so it is essential to give a child with diarrhoea plenty of liquids to drink.

2. A child with diarrhoea needs food.

170

3. When a breastfed child has diarrhoea, it is important to continue breastfeeding.

4. A child who is recovering from diarrhoea needs an extra meal every day for at least two weeks.

5. Trained help is needed if diarrhoea is more serious than usual, if it persists for more than two weeks, or if there is blood in the stool.

6. Medicines other than ORS should not be used for the diarrhoea, except on medical advice.

7. Diarrhoea can be prevented by breastfeeding, by immunizing all children against measles, by using latrines, by keeping food and water clean, and by washing hands before touching food.

See *Facts for Life* page 43 or *Children for Health* page 101 for supporting information.

Worms and parasites

Infection by common worms and parasites weaken millions of children and adults. Children with worms can be bad-tempered and tired and may not do well at school. Since the types of worms and parasites vary greatly, people in each area should make it a priority to inform themselves of what the threats are, how they can be countered and the best ways of treatment. Children can help younger brothers and sisters to avoid infection by teaching them good hygiene habits and not allowing them to play in places where they could be infected.

Prime messages

1. Although there are many different types of worms, all are parasites which live off us by taking food or sucking the blood inside us. All affect our growth and health in some way.

2. Worms in the intestine are all caused by poor sanitation and poor hygiene. Once these are improved it becomes easier to prevent worms. The eggs from worms are passed out into stools. Most worm eggs take over a week to become infectious so old stools are more dangerous than fresh ones. Good latrine habits are, therefore, vital to preventing and controlling worm infections.

3. When a child has worms it may not be noticed at first but worms multiply very fast and can be spread very easily. One unhygienic or careless person can infect many. Once one family member has worms all the family needs to be treated.

4. For intestinal worms such as roundworms, medicines are easily available and relatively cheap. Once children are free of worms they will feel better and study better.

5. Hookworm (among the most serious of worm infections) is transmitted though the skin. Wearing shoes helps reduce the risk of infection; so does stopping little children playing and crawling near places where stools are passed. Modern worm medicines have now been developed which can kill hookworm together with other worms.

6. Bilharzia, found mainly in Africa, breeds in still or slow-moving water. It uses snails as a host before entering the human body. In areas where it is common, every attempt must be made to identify sources of the disease, eliminate the snails and stop children swimming and wading in the water. Children must be discouraged from urinating in water that children may swim in.

See Child-to-Child *Resource Book 2* page 109 for further information.

Nutrition

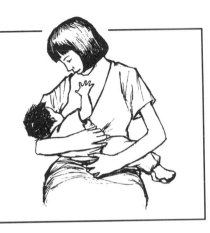

Breastfeeding

As future parents it is important for children to understand the importance of breastfeeding and the dangers of bottle-feeding. As carers of younger children it also of great importance for them to know the importance of good weaning practices, and how to make and to prepare good weaning foods.

Prime messages

1. Breast milk alone is the best possible food and drink for a baby. No other food or drink is needed for about the first six months of life.

2. Babies should start to breastfeed as soon as possible after birth. Virtually every mother can breastfeed her baby.

3. Breastfeeding causes more milk to be produced. A baby needs to suck frequently at the breast so that enough breast milk is produced to meet the baby's needs.

4. Breastfeeding helps to protect babies and young children against dangerous diseases. Bottle-feeding can lead to serious illness and death.

5. A variety of additional foods is necessary when a child is about six months old, but breastfeeding should continue well into the second year of a child's life and for longer if possible.

6. Breastfeeding gives a mother 98% protection against pregnancy for six months after giving birth *only if* her baby breastfeeds frequently, day and night, *and if* the baby is not regularly given other food and drink, *and if* the mother's periods have not returned.

See *Facts for Life* page 17 or *Children for Health* page 49 for supporting information.

Food for the family

As future parents, children need to know how to choose the best food available and affordable for *all* their family, as well as the importance of a mixed diet which gives all the elements which the body needs to grow and stay healthy and the mind to develop. They need to know the best means possible to grow food (even when land is limited) and to preserve the soil they have.

Prime messages

1. Children need food for their minds as well as their bodies. Good food in the first years increases potential for doing well at school and living a successful and happy life.

2. All children need access to the best food available in the family; girls as well as boys, children as well as adults.

3. All children need to be given the opportunity and encouragement to eat frequently. They need a wide variety of available food to help their growth.

4. Orange or yellow fruits and vegetables, and dark green leafy vegetables, are easy to grow and necessary for providing vitamins which protect the body from illness. A small amount of oil is necessary in the every diet because it helps the body absorb certain important vitamins.

5. Soil is a resource that cannot be replaced. With more people in the world there is a greater need to make better use of it. Families should preserve and enrich their soil for themselves and their descendants.

See *Children for Health* page 173 for supplementary information.

Note: three micronutrients

1. Vitamin A
Why we need it
Vitamin A helps the body to fight disease, and it is also important for healthy eyes. If we do not have sufficient vitamin A we risk getting more common diseases such as diarrhoea and measles, and we have a higher chance of dying from infection.

How we can get it
Babies get enough vitamin A from breast milk, and this is a particularly important source during diarrhoea. Vitamin A is contained in orange and yellow fruit and dark green leafy vegetables, and when these are cooked with oil (to help absorption) vitamin A intake is improved. When people's diets lack vitamin A special vitamin capsules can be given three times a year. They are not very expensive.

2. Iodine
Why we need it
Our bodies need iodine to produce the thyroid hormone from the small gland at the bottom of the neck. If we do not get enough iodine, the thyroid glands swell (goitre) and lack of thyroid hormone causes poor development of the brain, both during the time of development in the womb and during childhood. Soils in mountainous and repeatedly flooded areas are deficient in iodine and people living in these areas are prone to goitre.

How we can get it
Iodine can also be put back into our bodies if the tiny amounts we need are added to the salt we use. Many governments have programmes to make sure that 'iodized salt' or oils are available and these are quite safe to use. Schools should recommend them. Iodine can also be added to water supplies and given as capsules.

3. Iron
Why we need it
Iron is necessary for producing good strong red blood-cells, to prevent anaemia. It is necessary for the healthy functioning of the brain and the body. Intestinal worm infections, particularly hookworm, cause iron deficiency.

How can we get it
Better nutrition helps – eating more vegetables such as spinach, and more cereals. So does preventing and treating hookworm. When there are severe problems iron tablets can be given to all school children. They are completely safe but need to be given regularly and therefore may cost more than schools can afford unless outside programmes can fund them.

Theme 3

Growth and development

Child growth

As future parents and as family members, children need to know the importance of monitoring the growth of babies and the fact that when a young child does not gain weight there is need to seek help. They may be able to help their parents weigh and record weight of babies and explain why this is important.

Prime messages

1. Children from birth to the age of three years should be weighed every month. If there is no weight gain for two months something is wrong.

2. Breast milk alone is the best possible food for about the first six months of a child s life.

3. By the age of six months the child needs other food in addition to breast milk.

4. A child under five needs food five or six times a day.

5. A child under three years of age needs a small amount of fat or oil added to the family's ordinary food.

6. All children need foods rich in Vitamin A: breast milk, green leafy vegetables and orange-coloured fruits and vegetables.

7. After an illness a child needs one extra meal every day for at least a week.

See *Facts for Life* page 27 or *Children for Health* page 61 for supporting information.

> ### Small children have small stomachs. Feed them often.

Child development

As future parents, children need to understand the importance of helping children's minds develop. They have a key role to play in stimulating younger brothers and sisters, playing with them, making toys for them and encouraging them to talk and develop coordination.

Prime messages

1. Babies begin to learn rapidly from the moment they are born. By age two, most of the growth of the human brain is already complete. For good mental growth, the child's greatest need is the love and attention of adults.

2. Play is important to a child's development. By playing, a child exercises mind and body, and absorbs basic lessons about the world. Parents can help a child to play.

3. Children learn how to behave by imitating the behaviour of those closest to them.

4. Young children easily become angry, frightened, and tearful. Patience, understanding, and sympathy with the child's emotions will help the child to grow up happy, well balanced, and well behaved.

5. Children need frequent approval and encouragement. Physical punishment is bad for a child s development.

6. The foundations of learning well in school can be built by the parents in the earliest years of a child's life.

7. A parent is the best observer of a child's development. So all parents should know the warning signs which mean that a child is not making normal progress and that something may be wrong.

See *Facts for Life* page 85 or *Children for Health* page 73 for supporting information.

Safe motherhood

As future parents *all* children (girls *and* boys) need to be aware of the importance of timing births, the dangers of early pregnancy and the risks associated with some traditional birth practices. It is only through education that such practices and customs can be changed.

Prime messages

1. Becoming pregnant before the age of 18, or after the age of 35, increases the risk for both mother and child.

2. The risk of death for young children is increased by about 50% if the space between births is less than two years.

3. Having more than four children increases the health risks of pregnancy and childbirth.

4. There are many safe and acceptable ways of avoiding pregnancy. Family planning services can give couples the knowledge and the means to plan when to begin having children, how far apart to have them, and when to stop.

5. The risks of childbirth can be drastically reduced by going to the nearest health worker for regular check-ups during pregnancy.

6. A trained person should assist at every birth.

7. To reduce the dangers of pregnancy and childbirth, all families should know the warning signs.

8. All women need more food during pregnancy. All need more rest.

9. Spacing pregnancies at least two years apart, and avoiding pregnancies below the age of 18 or above the age of 35, drastically reduces the dangers of child-bearing.

See *Facts for Life* pages 1 and 9 and *Children for Health* page 158 for supplementary information.

Theme 4

Infectious diseases

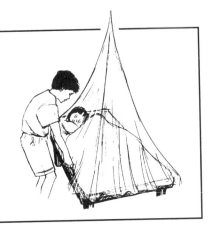

Malaria

Malaria affects millions of people worldwide and kills large numbers of children. As future parents and family members, children need to know how mosquitoes breed and when they are most dangerous. They can contribute to malarial control programmes both nationally and locally by helping to prevent mosquitoes from breeding and from biting people. They can also learn to help a child with fever by preventing the temperature from rising too high and giving the sick child plenty of liquids.

Prime messages

1. Young children should be protected from mosquito bites, especially at night. Nets are the best protection against malaria; those treated with insecticide are especially effective.

2. Communities should destroy mosquito larvae and prevent mosquitoes from breeding by ensuring there are no pools of water near houses.

3. Wherever malaria is common, pregnant women should take anti-malarial tablets throughout pregnancy.

4. Wherever malaria is common, a child who has a fever should be taken immediately to a health worker. If malaria appears to be the cause, the child should be given a full course of an anti-malarial drug.

5. A child with a fever must drink frequently. ORS solution replaces salt as well as water lost through sweating.

6. A child with a fever should be kept cool but not cold. A child with a very high temperature (fever) is in danger of fits which can cause brain damage.

7. A child recovering from a fever (or other disease) needs plenty of liquids and food.

See *Facts for Life* page 69 or *Children for Health* page 135 for supplementary information.

Immunization

As future parents, all children need to understand when and why babies should be immunized. Immunization campaigns worldwide have already helped to save millions of lives and children in all countries have played a part in them. However, much more needs to be done to persuade all families to bring all children to be immunized at the right time and to complete the full course of immunizations.

Prime messages

1. Immunization protects against several dangerous diseases. A child who is not immunized is more likely to become undernourished, to become disabled, and to die.

2. Immunization is urgent. All immunizations should be completed in the first year of the child s life.

3. It is safe to immunize a sick child.

4. Every woman between the age of 15 and 44 should be fully immunized against tetanus.

See *Facts for Life* page 35 or *Children for Health* page 115 for supporting information.

Immunization schedule for Infants*	
Age	**Disease to be immunized against**
Birth	Tuberculosis (and polio in some countries)
6 weeks	Diphtheria, whooping cough, tetanus, polio
10 weeks	Diphtheria, whooping cough, tetanus, polio
14 weeks	Diphtheria, whooping cough, tetanus, polio
9 months	Measles (12-15 months in industrialized countries) and polio in some countries

* National immunization schedules may differ slightly from country to country.

Coughs and colds

Everyone gets coughs and colds. Most coughs and colds get better without special medicine. But sometimes colds turn into pneumonia. Four million children die of pneumonia every year. Signs of pneumonia include quick breathing that is more difficult than usual (sometimes accompanied by grunting). As future parents and as family members, children need to know:

* the importance of looking after others with coughs and colds, and encouraging them to eat and drink;
* that buying expensive medicines such as antibiotics cannot help and may harm children;
* how to recognize danger signs of pneumonia and warn parents to get medical help quickly.

Prime messages

1. If a child with a cough is breathing much more rapidly than normal, then the child is at risk. It is essential to get the child to a clinic quickly.

2. Families can help prevent pneumonia by making sure that babies are breastfed for at least the first six months of life and that children are well nourished and fully immunized.

3. A child with a cough or cold should be helped to eat and to drink plenty of liquids.

4. A child with a cough or cold should be kept warm but not hot, and should breathe clean, non-smoky air.

See *Facts for Life* page 53 or *Children for Health* page 125 for supporting information.

Theme 5

Safety and safe lifestyles

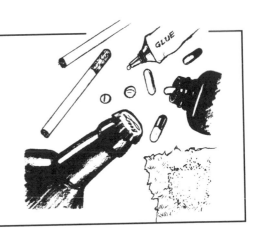

Accidents

Nearly all accidents can be prevented. All children have a prime role in teaching younger children to stay safe in the home and on the roads. They also have a role in making adults aware of the risks children face through unsafe practices and careless behaviour. Many simple first-aid practices can be learnt by all children.

Prime messages

1. Children under four years old are particularly at risk in the home. This is where most deaths and serious accidents occur. Almost all can be prevented.

2. Families need to take special care to make their home environment safe and to watch little children to prevent them from unsafe behaviour. Remember that houses are not designed for children, particularly children under two. Try always to look at safety in the home with a young child in mind, and take action such as making sure no dangerous fluids, e.g. paraffin, are left in jars from which children can drink.

3. Places where children often play should be made as safe as possible. All glass bottles should be banned. In some countries there is also a great risk of drowning. Older children must learn to take responsibility for the safety of younger ones at play.

4. Children under five years old are particularly at risk on the roads. They should be watched and taught safety behaviour as soon as they can walk.

5. All families need to know simple first aid – particularly that related to burns, cuts and wounds, and swallowing poisons and other objects. Many common practices are dangerous to health.

See *Children for Health* page 163 for supplementary information.

Substance abuse

Many of us think that the term 'drugs' applies to those illegal drugs such as heroin and cocaine. In fact even more harm is done by the wrong use of medicines and by the addictive drugs, alcohol and nicotine, which are readily available to everyone. Children, therefore, need to learn and pass on not only the dangers of trying out 'hard drugs' but also the serious effects of buying and using unnecessary or unprescribed medicines, as well as the great dangers caused by smoking and by taking too much alcohol.

Prime messages

1. Often when we are not well we do not need medicines. In many cases it is enough to rest and to have plenty to drink and good food to help the body fight off the disease and get better.

2. Taking medicines unnecessarily (e.g. antibiotics for a cold) can be harmful. It wastes money and helps germs resist the medicine when it is needed.

3. When medicines are necessary they are only safe and effective when they are taken according to instructions. The full course of medicines must always be taken. Taking too much or too little medicine can both be harmful. Adult medicines can be dangerous for children.

4. Injections are not usually better than medicines taken by mouth. Receiving an injection from an untrained person can be very dangerous.

5. Medicines are dangerous to young children. They must be kept out of reach.

6. Certain drugs are known as 'addictive' because they cause users to become dependent on them. When they stop using these drugs they have more or less serious side effects. Some of these drugs, such as heroin and cocaine, have very serious effects on health.

7. Alcohol and nicotine (from cigarettes) are both addictive drugs. Both cause more deaths and distress than the 'hard' drugs such as heroin. Both can be very dangerous to pregnant women and affect the health of unborn babies.

See Child-to-Child *Resource Book 1* page 00 for further information.

AIDS

HIV, the virus which causes AIDS, kills by damaging the body's defences against other diseases. Millions of people worldwide are affected and millions of uninfected children will be orphaned by AIDS during the coming years. Children have a key role in protecting themselves, spreading messages to others and helping those who have AIDS or who have been left without parents. They must appreciate that people infected with HIV and AIDS in families and communities need help and friendship from other community members, including children.

Prime messages

1. AIDS is an incurable disease. It is caused by a virus which can be passed on by sexual intercourse, by infected blood, by dirty hypodermic needles (sometimes used by drug users or used for injections by unqualified persons), and by infected mothers to their unborn children.

2. People who are sure that both they and their partner are uninfected and have no other sex partners are not at risk from AIDS. People who know or suspect that this might not be the case should practise safer sex. This means either sex without intercourse (penetration), or intercourse only when protected by a condom.

3. When people have other sexually transmitted diseases (STDs) the risk of their spreading and catching the HIV virus is greatly increased.

4. Women infected with HIV should think carefully about having a baby and should seek advice. There is a one-in-three chance that their babies will also be born infected with HIV.

5. All parents should tell their children how HIV is spread.

See *Facts for Life* page 77 and *Children for Health* page 143 for supplementary information.

Theme 6

Working with Disabled People

Most disabled people can live satisfying and fulfilling lives if society allows them to do so. Society often dispenses pity on disabled people, which is cheap and useless, instead of investing time and money in preventing the causes of disability and providing the facilities to enable those who are disabled so that they may live as effective and happy citizens. Everyone in a society needs to feel personally involved in promoting the rights of disabled persons to live and work as others do. Disabled people's organizations can often help us to clarify needs and suggest ways through which they can be met.

Prime messages

1. There are different kinds and degrees of disability, both physical and mental. Some causes of disability are preventable (e.g. polio, accidents).

2. Often those with disabilities such as poor sight and hearing, learning difficulties or poor mobility are hidden by families or denied access to work because of lack of understanding of what their disability is, how it affects their lives and how it its effects can be minimized. Knowledge about disabilities is a starting point for being able to manage them.

3. Often the greatest difficulties which disabled persons face is the attitude of the communities in which they live. What is needed is for communities to do their utmost to enable disabled persons to lead fulfilled lives. Disabled people do not wish to be considered 'special', only to have help to overcome the problems which their disability causes for them – such as not seeing, hearing, understanding, or moving about in the way that others do. Often very simple actions such as providing access or employment for disabled persons can change their lives.

4. Disabled children need to be accepted by other children as friends and fellow pupils. They should be helped only when necessary and never pitied.

5. Children and adults who are not disabled need to give thought to how a disability shapes other people's lives and how disabled children and adults may like others to act towards them.

See Child-to-Child *Resource Book Part 2* Section 5; also see Werner D., *Disabled Village Children* (details on page 166).

NOTE
Coping with adolescence: how our bodies and emotions change at puberty

The physical and emotional changes that occur around puberty can cause girls and boys great confusion and stress. It is important that young people have an opportunity to learn the facts about their development and are able to discuss their concerns openly with each other and with a sympathetic, non-judgmental adult. This will help them to pass through puberty and adolescence with knowledge, confidence and self-esteem.

Main topics:

1. Why our bodies change
A natural process in developing from a child into a sexually mature adult able to produce children.

2. How our bodies change
Main facts about our bodies and the changes which take place in boys and girls.

3. Personal hygiene
Including during menstruation.

4. Local beliefs and practices
Some beliefs attach a sense of shame, guilt or 'impurity' to physical processes such as menstruation. Adolescents need to accept them as natural and normal.

5. Emotional changes
Young people need to realize that they may become:
- more self-conscious about their behaviours and more concerned about what others (especially those of their age) think about them;
- more subject to pressure to take risks;
- more interested in the opposite sex.

6. Behaviour changes in adults and young persons
- Expectations of families and of society may change greatly, especially for girls.
- Adolescents may seek more independence from their family and may challenge parents' authority.
- Friends and other young people become more important examples than parents or teachers.
- Adolescents may experiment with new relationships with the same or the opposite sex.

7. Concerns young people have
In relation to their own cultures young people need to learn and discuss:
- sexual reproduction
- sexual health
- the age of maturity for sexual relationships and pregnancy
- contraception
- sexually transmitted diseases (STDs) and AIDS (see page 179)
- sexual identity
- sexual abuse or molestation
- substance abuse (see page 178)
- risk taking, e.g. leaving home, gang fights, etc.

8. Life skills and values
In order to achieve self-respect and to develop satisfying and trusting family and social relation ships, adolescents need support in:
- developing life skills (e.g. coping with stress, resisting pressures;
- clarifying values related to social and sexual behaviour;
- making their own responsible decisions based on these values.

Index